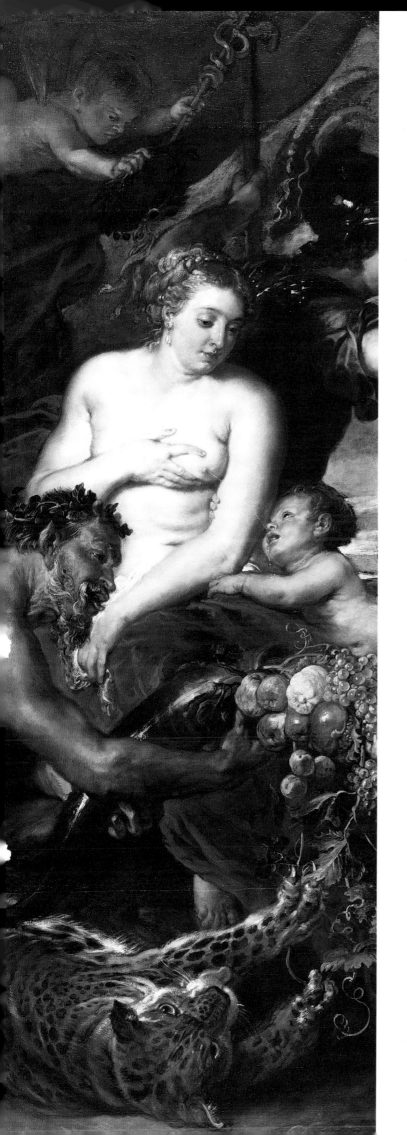

National Gallery Technical Bulletin

Volume 20, 1999

Painting in Antwerp
and London:
Rubens and Van Dyck

National Gallery Publications
London

Distributed by
Yale University Press

Series Editor: Ashok Roy

First published in Great Britain in 1999
by National Gallery Publications Limited
St Vincent House, 30 Orange Street
London WC2H 7HH

British Library Cataloguing in Publication Data
A catalogue record for this journal is available
from the British Library

ISBN 1 85709 251 1
ISSN 0140 7430
525278

Edited by Diana Davies and Jan Green
Page make-up by John Gibbs
Printed in Great Britain by BAS Printers Limited,
Over Wallop, Hampshire

Front cover
Anthony van Dyck, Detail of Lady Thimbelby from *Lady
Elizabeth Thimbelby and Dorothy, Viscountess Andover*
(see Plate 34, p. 74).

Page one
Peter Paul Rubens, Detail from '*Peace and War*'
(see Plate 1, p. 90).

Contents

Preface

THIS *TECHNICAL BULLETIN* is the second to be devoted to a single subject: the painting techniques and studio practice of Rubens and Van Dyck.[1] This year, 1999, is the 400th anniversary of Anthony van Dyck's birth in Antwerp where he became, for about five years before the start of his independent career, one of Rubens's most successful and prodigious collaborators. Van Dyck's anniversary is being celebrated by a major exhibition of his work at the Koninklijk Museum voor Schone Kunsten in Antwerp and subsequently at the Royal Academy in London. This exhibition is organised and curated by our former colleague at the National Gallery, Dr Christopher Brown, now Director of the Ashmolean Museum in Oxford, who has always had a keen interest in technical studies of Flemish and Dutch seventeenth-century pictures.

The National Gallery's collection of paintings by Van Dyck is exceptionally strong and broad in range, and there have been a number of important acquisitions over the past twenty years. As with all great painters, simply to describe Van Dyck's painting methods and materials would go only a certain way in explaining his technique, which involves also an unparalleled brilliance of design and execution. But, as Jo Kirby explains in her account of the painter's trade in the seventeenth century, both Rubens and Van Dyck were fully immersed in what had developed in the Low Countries as widely accepted painting practice under the general control of the Guild of St Luke, although Rubens's position as court painter to the Governors of the Spanish Netherlands exempted him from certain of the Guild's requirements. The painting methods employed by these two great painters can be seen as representative of the work of many Antwerp practitioners, although their painterly skills were clearly exceptional and regarded as such during their lifetimes. Since Rubens and Van Dyck both travelled extensively and their work became well known in a number of the courts of Europe, influences on their own practice, particularly from Italy, are evident in their methods of painting and in turn their influence was felt widely, particularly in England through the patronage of Charles I and the court.

Jo Kirby's comprehensive introductory overview covers the guilds and the training of painters, painters' treatises, studio organisation, and the materials and methods of painting on a variety of supports. This volume also contains a survey of Van Dyck's technical procedures and their development through his career as seen in the National Gallery's paintings. Raymond White has contributed the first compilation to be published of Van Dyck's paint media, based on analyses using gas-chromatography linked to mass-spectrometry. The evolution of the composition of Rubens's large allegorical painting, usually known as '*Peace and War*', is explored in the light of new information derived from the X-radiograph and paint layer structure examination, and Larry Keith of the Conservation Department tackles the difficult question of studio participation in Rubens's canvas painting in his account of the *Drunken Silenus supported by Satyrs*.

The authors would like to thank colleagues at the National Gallery for their helpful comments on the manuscripts, particularly Neil MacGregor, Nicholas Penny and David Jaffé, and Christopher Brown in Oxford. We would also like to thank Marika Spring and Véronique Tissières, Intern in the Scientific Department during 1997–98, for their help in technical examination of the paintings discussed in this issue, and Diana Davies and Jan Green for their customary painstaking editing and editorial management of the *Bulletin*.

ASHOK ROY

---

1. Volume 18 of the *National Gallery Technical Bulletin*, published in 1997, is also a special issue dealing with early Northern European painting from 1400 to 1550.

The Painter's Trade in the Seventeenth Century: Theory and Practice

JO KIRBY

THE CAREERS of Peter Paul Rubens and his most talented assistant, Anthony van Dyck, unfolded during a period of relative prosperity in Antwerp. The city no longer had the total commercial dominance it had had some fifty years earlier, but it had recovered from a period of violent struggle and economic collapse. This, together with the powerful stimulus of the Counter-Reformation, created a constant demand for the production of art works and architectural projects. There was plenty of work to be had at home and, although the reputation of Rubens was such that he could command the highest prices, many other artists also prospered: Jacob Jordaens, for example, born into already comfortable circumstances, died an extremely wealthy man owning much property after a long and successful career. However, to a greater extent than their compatriots, Rubens and Van Dyck also had an international aspect to their careers and, in addition, much of their work was for royal or court patrons. Rubens worked for aristocratic patrons in Mantua, Rome and other Italian cities, as well as for the courts of Spain, France, England and the Spanish Netherlands itself, in Brussels. Van Dyck worked in Genoa and Rome, in Brussels and in London. Indeed, the influence of Van Dyck's style and techniques on English painting cannot be overstated. Both artists were enormously prolific and could not have produced such a vast quantity of work without studio assistance; this is particularly true of Rubens, who is known to have maintained a large studio, and whose level of production is all the more astonishing when it is remembered that between 1626 and 1630 he also had a busy and successful diplomatic career.

From a technical point of view, any painting must be considered in the context of where it was produced and what materials or methods were used. In the case of Van Dyck, who worked abroad for long periods of time, it may be possible to assess the extent of the variation between the materials available in one centre and in another. The National Gallery is fortunate in that the work of both Van Dyck and Rubens, throughout their careers, is well represented in the Collection. In addition, some comparison can be made with the materials used by contemporary painters in Antwerp, London and Rome.

Antwerp

Antwerp's position as the principal commercial centre of Northern Europe, built on sea trade and the textile industry, declined during the 1570s and after years of unrest the city fell to the troops of Philip II of Spain in 1585. As a result of the general migration from the largely Catholic Southern Netherlands the population of Antwerp decreased from about 80,000 in 1584–5 to about 48,400 in October 1586.[1]

Rubens was born in 1577 in Siegen, Germany, of parents who were natives of Antwerp. His widowed mother brought her family back to Antwerp in about 1588, the same year that Anthony van Dyck's father, Frans, set up his business in the city as a merchant in silk, ribbons and similar goods. When Van Dyck was born in 1599, his father was quite wealthy; indeed, there had been a gradual improvement in the fortunes of the Southern Netherlands in general. The Twelve Years Truce between Spain and the Dutch provinces from 1609 to 1621 permitted a more sustained revival, under the sympathetic governorship of Archduke Albert of Austria and his wife Isabella, daughter of Philip II of Spain. Much of Antwerp's revitalised trade was in luxury goods, like those dealt in by Van Dyck's father and the silk merchant Daniel Fourment, the father of Rubens's second wife, Helena: silk and tapestry; diamond processing; precious metalwork and fine furniture. The city became the centre for goods moving between the north and the south as Antwerp entrepreneurs benefited from trading links they were able to develop with former emigrants, who had set up in business in the northern cities where they had settled.

The impact of the Counter-Reformation on the revival of the Southern Netherlands, and the renewal of education in, and devotion to, the Catholic faith, cannot be overestimated. Catholic literature and religious prints were produced in enormous numbers by Antwerp presses and Antwerp printers flourished. Nowhere is this influence clearer than in architecture and the arts. New churches were built; old ones were modernised in the Baroque style; devotional paintings were required and produced in large quantity. The activity was not confined to ecclesiastical work; it extended into more secular decorative projects and portraiture and court patronage, both in the Spanish Netherlands and abroad.[2]

Netherlandish Painters in London

From the latter part of the sixteenth century and through the seventeenth, there was a tradition of painters from the Low Countries working and forming communities abroad, as they did in Rome, for example. The reasons were partly economic, partly religious: many were refugees from the consequences of the long struggle between the Netherlands and Spain. They tended to find work at

Plate 1 Daniel Mytens, *Alatheia Talbot, Countess of Arundel, c.*1618. Canvas, 207 × 127 cm. London, National Portrait Gallery (no. 5293).

court, not only in London but also in other Northern European centres such as Copenhagen and Prague.[3] Undoubtedly the overall technical competence of painters trained in the Netherlands and their mastery of the depiction of surfaces, textures and fastidious detail would have been a factor in their popularity with aristocratic patrons. Local artists, however, felt some resentment at the fact that prestigious commissions went to foreign painters. Henry Peacham, who was a Norfolk schoolmaster and, briefly, tutor to the sons of Thomas Howard, Earl of Arundel, before turning to a literary career in London, lamented in the *Epistle dedicatorie* to his manual *Graphice* (London 1612): 'Onely I am sory that our courtiers and great personages must seeke farre and neere for some Dutchman or Italian to draw their pictures, and invent their devises, our Englishmen being held for *Vaunients* [i.e. worthless persons].'[4]

When Van Dyck was invited to England in 1620, he followed on the heels of Paul van Somer (*c.*1576–1622, from Antwerp) and Daniel Mytens (*c.*1590–1647, from Delft); Mytens, appointed by Charles I as his 'picture-drawer' for life in 1625 (Plate 1), was later supplanted by Van Dyck on his return in 1632.[5] Van Somer in his turn had taken over at the court of James I from John de Critz the Elder (died 1642) and Marcus Gheeraerts the Younger (died 1636), both of whom were members of families fleeing Spanish persecutions in the Netherlands in 1568.[6] Some local painters did obtain court patronage: Robert Peake and William Larkin (both of whom died in 1619) at the court of James I, and later Cornelis Jonson, appointed a picture-maker to Charles I in 1632 (Plate 2). Jonson was of German/Dutch stock and may well have received some of his training in the Netherlands. A good painter, but unable to compete with the flair and superlative skills of Van Dyck, he retired to Kent and in 1643, after the outbreak of the English Civil War, moved permanently to Utrecht.[7]

Guilds and the Training of Artists

In Antwerp painters trained in the studio of a master, under the control of the Guild of Saint Luke, much as in previous centuries. The master registered his young apprentices with the Guild on payment of a fee, and after several years' training (perhaps with more than one master), if the Guild was satisfied with the apprentice's work, he was registered as a free master. As well as the painters and panel- and frame-makers (who perhaps made up the majority of free masters), craftsmen in other related trades – printers, book-

Plate 2 Cornelis Jonson, *Thomas Coventry, 1st Baron Coventry*, 1639. Canvas, 126.4 × 100.3 cm. London, National Portrait Gallery (no. 4815).

Fig. 1 Anthony van Dyck, *Hendrick van Balen*, 1627–32. Black chalk on paper, 24.3 × 19.8 cm. Malibu, J. Paul Getty Museum (no. 84.GB.92).

binders, those working in the glass and pottery trades, embroiderers and goldsmiths – became free masters of the Guild.[8] Painters were not only simply registered as *schilders*: some are described as *doekschilders* (painters on cloth or canvas), *waterverf-* or *waterschilders* (painters in watercolour), *geconterfeytschilders* (portrait painters), *huiss childers* (house painters), and, by the 1630s, *lantschapschilders* (landscape painters) and *bloemschilders* (flower painters). Painters who had received their training elsewhere, but came to live and work in Antwerp, were required to enrol in the Antwerp Guild; the records for 1634–5 include the name of the Leiden painter Jan Lievens, who had first moved to London (where he met Van Dyck while working at court) and subsequently to Antwerp.[9]

Rubens is not recorded as an apprentice, although it is thought that he trained with Tobias Verhaecht, Adam van Noort – whose other pupils included Jacob Jordaens (in 1607) – and Otto van Veen. He was admitted as a master in 1598.[10] Jordaens became a master in 1615, being described as a *waterschilder*.[11] In 1609 Van Dyck was apprenticed at the age of ten years to the figure painter Hendrick van Balen (Fig. 1), who painted small, decorative pictures and had a busy studio in Antwerp (Plate 3).[12] It is not known when Van Dyck entered Rubens's studio, but the portrait of Van Dyck painted by Rubens in about 1615 (now in the Rubenshuis, Antwerp) suggests that he was a member of his studio by this time and possibly earlier. The association continued until 1620, two years after he had become a master, when he is the only named assistant in the contract for the cycle of paintings on the ceiling of the Jesuit Church, Antwerp (destroyed by fire in 1718).[13] As court painter to the Governors of the Spanish Netherlands Rubens was exempted from the rules of the Guild and was not obliged to register the names of his apprentices (although he did register one, Jacques Moermans, in 1621–2).[14]

Little is known about the teaching the pupils received in the master's studio at this time. They probably began by drawing: by copying the master's drawings and perhaps published engravings; by drawing from casts and other objects in the studio, such as drapery; and by drawing from the life. Inventories of the properties of artists and of the contents of their studios show that busy and successful painters, like Hendrick van Balen, possessed drawings, books of prints and plaster casts

Plate 3 Hendrick van Balen the Elder and a follower of Jan Brueghel the Elder, *Pan pursuing Syrinx* (NG 659), possibly after 1615. Copper, 25 × 19.4 cm.

that would have been suitable as teaching aids.[15] By copying, the pupil would learn how to assemble the elements of a composition; he would also learn how the paint was prepared and how to apply it. As the apprentice developed, he would progress to transferring the master's composition to the prepared support, working from a drawing or sketch; finally he would be sufficiently competent to lay in the composition for final correction and touching-up by the master. At this stage the apprentice could be more accurately described as an assistant.

In the period during which Van Dyck is likely to have been working in Rubens's studio, the majority of Rubens's apprentices seem to have received their basic training elsewhere; whether this was common practice or a particular feature of his studio, because it was extraordinarily busy and the competition to enter it was intense, is not known.[16] There was at this time no question of a more 'academic' artistic education for the young painter.

In London the painters' trade was regulated by the Painter-Stainers' Company. The Company appears to have acquired a degree of authority and recognition only relatively late in its history, being granted a Royal Charter by Elizabeth I in 1581. This was given after they had presented a petition to the Queen in 1575, complaining of their inability to control the number of foreign painters in the City and the quality of the work done. At this date freemen of the Company fell into various categories: Face Painters, History Painters, Arms Painters (responsible for heraldry) and House Painters. Among the thirty-seven articles in the Charter, one forbade anyone 'English or stranger, denizen or not, freeman or foreign' to do any work connected with painting in any form unless they were known to be skilful and approved. Various dues had to be paid by all those living within a four-mile radius of the City; foreigners were subject to the same dues, conditions and penalties as the English painters. Nobody was permitted to paint unless an apprenticeship of seven years with a painter had been served, except for 'gentlemen' pursuing the art as 'recreation or private pleasure': it is noteworthy that the interest in painting as a pleasurable activity for amateurs had grown to the point where such an exception was necessary. At the end of their apprenticeship the apprentices were examined and their work approved by the Master and Wardens of the Company. The number of apprentices that a member was permitted to have was limited and apprentices had to be presented to the Master and Wardens of the Company within a certain period, or else a fine was payable. As in Antwerp, this enabled the Company to keep a measure of control over the number of masters working, in theory at least. There were penalties for deceitful work and the Company officials were empowered to search premises for faulty goods or materials.[17]

The London guild waged a constant battle, not only with foreign painters, but also with members of other guilds, particularly those of the heralds and the plasterers, who often carried out rather similar work.[18] Part of the problem lay in the fact that, in earlier times, the painters had undertaken many lucrative, largely decorative, court commissions, but these were increasingly being given to foreign artists. In 1627, for example, a petition was presented to Charles I by a group of picture-makers, supported by the Painter-Stainers' Company, complaining that painters like Daniel Mytens, Orazio Gentileschi and others (all employed at court) were taking their livelihood. The dispute was partly resolved when in 1636 the Royal Surveyor, Inigo Jones (a member of the Company), was brought in as mediator.[19] The attempt to encourage good relations between all the warring parties appears to be marked by an invitation to Van Dyck to attend the St Katherine's Dinner on

30 November 1637 at the Painter-Stainers' Hall in the ward of Queenhithe; the other guests included Inigo Jones, John de Critz, the King's Sergeant Painter (the official responsible for arranging all the painted work for the court) and his wife, and Edward Norgate, the Windsor Herald.[20]

In order to practise a trade, it was necessary to become a freeman of a City company, but one of the simplest expedients to evade this requirement was to live outside the City walls. It has been shown that many painters lived just to the north-west or west of the City, in the parishes of St Giles-without-Cripplegate, St Andrew Holborn, St Sepulchre-without-Newgate (also in Holborn) and St Bride Fleet Street parishes. Another popular location, further west – and nearer the court – was Westminster, and particularly the parishes of St Martin-in-the-Fields and, rather later, the new parish of St Paul Covent Garden, created in its northern part. Very few lived within the City walls.[21] Marcus Gheeraerts the Younger and his son, also named Marcus, were two of the very few who did: they lived in Warwick Lane, in the parish of Christchurch Newgate Street in the ward of Farringdon Within and both were freemen of the Painter-Stainers' Company. The name of Marcus Gheeraerts the Younger, as 'Marcus Garret/ Garrett' is recorded as a 'stranger' living in the parish in 1598/9, and also in a list of aliens living in the City of London made in 1618.[22] In 1632, Van Dyck stayed with Edward Norgate until he moved into accommodation on the waterside at Blackfriars, within the City of London, in the parish of St Anne. This parish was home to many miniature painters, and also to Cornelis Jonson, and because it was the site of a former monastic foundation – and therefore a 'liberty' or 'precinct' of the City – its residents claimed various privileges, including the freedom for all artists and craftsmen, whether they were freemen of the City or not, to practise their trade without interference from the authorities. This was particularly attractive to foreign painters who had no right of citizenship unless they had become denizens of the City by right.[23]

A great many Northern European painters, including those from the North and South Netherlands, chose to spend some time in Italy at some point in their careers to broaden their artistic experience; most visited Rome. Here, in the latter part of the sixteenth and early seventeenth centuries, the guild system had less control over painters and sculptors than in Antwerp or most other Netherlandish cities, but there was some concern at

Plate 4 Paolo Veronese, *Allegory of Love, I* (*'Unfaithfulness'*) (NG 1318), probably 1570s. Canvas, 189.9 × 189.9 cm. This composition was recorded in Van Dyck's Italian sketchbook.

the perceived ignorance of young painters. Popes Gregory XIII and, later, Sixtus V both supported the suggestion that an academy for the education of artists was necessary, presumably in addition to the training they received with a master, and the Accademia di San Luca was inaugurated in 1593. Its first president was Federigo Zuccaro, and its primary aim was educational; a lecture programme was instituted and life classes were held.[24] Netherlandish artists visiting Rome enjoyed the relative looseness of control by the painters' guild and formed a close and somewhat riotous community, as Van Dyck found to his cost.[25] Antwerp painters who had visited or worked in Rome were enrolled in the guild of Romanists, which numbered among its members not only Rubens and Van Dyck, but also Van Dyck's first master, Hendrick van Balen the Elder, Jan Brueghel the Elder, a close friend of Rubens, and Frans Snijders, one of several artists known to have collaborated with Rubens. In practice, the Academy did not have complete ascendancy over the painters' guild and in 1633 the guild levied a compulsory tax on all painters, including foreigners, much to their annoyance. It was also a fairly common practice in Italy, although not at this time in Northern Europe, for groups of artists to gather together to draw from nude models; these informal associations were also known as Academies.[26] Edward Norgate described such an Academy in his *Miniatura or the Art of Limning* (*c.*1648) and added that Rubens had told him that 'at his being in Italy, divers of his nation had followed this Academicall course for twenty Yeares together to little or noe purpose'.[27]

The influence of the work of contemporary Italian painters such as Caravaggio is immediately apparent in the work of artists of the Utrecht School such as Hendrick ter Brugghen and Gerrit van Honthorst, and it also impressed Rubens. For Van Dyck the Venetian masters of the previous century, Titian and Veronese, were of the greatest interest (Plate 4). Rubens spent eight years in Italy from 1600 to 1608 in the service of Vincenzo Gonzaga, Duke of Mantua. He also visited Spain, where he was able to see the Titians and other works in the Royal collection. Van Dyck travelled widely in Italy between 1621 and 1627, spending most time in Genoa.

Contemporary Written Sources

The painting practices and materials of seventeenth-century artists are reasonably well documented, but much useful information may also be gained from legal and commercial records: inventories, accounts, wills, price lists, records of import and export of materials, records of duties payable and so forth. Frequently, in both London and Rome, for example, much of this documentary evidence is lodged in archives and has not been the subject of research; even where it is quite well known, it may be unpublished. It is certain, therefore, that a great deal remains to be discovered on painting practice in this period. Sources fall into two broad categories: artists' handbooks and the more technical literature on seventeenth-century painting materials and methods; and literature associated with particular artists.[28]

A certain amount of information on the different materials and their making may sometimes be gained from artists' manuals, although as a rule these are more concerned with preparation of the materials for use, not their manufacture. However, an exception was often made in the case of methods for the preparation of oils and, particularly, varnishes. A good example of an Italian manuscript collection which describes not only the pigments, their sources and the theory of their mixtures, based on Giovanni Paolo Lomazzo's *Trattato dell' arte della pittura, scoltura e architettura* (Milan 1584), but also recipes for varnishes, watercolour pigments, inks and glues, some very traditional and others apparently up-to-date, is the so-called Paduan manuscript (the name given it by its nineteenth-century transcriber, Mrs Merrifield). Written in Venice, probably in the mid-

to late seventeenth century, it represents the type and range of technical information that would have been current around the time Van Dyck was in Italy.[29] The manufacture or purification of pigments, or glass, or pottery, was essentially a workshop-based technology, although one need only look at the large quantities of raw materials used by the Pekstok company in Amsterdam in the production of a yellow lake pigment from buckthorn to realise that some firms operated on a very large scale.[30] The recipes they used for their day-to-day preparations were generally kept secret; the records kept by Willem Pekstok and his fellows in other technologies are rare survivals.

A popular form of technical literature, the books of 'secrets', often derive their information from much older manuscript collections. The recipes they contain on pigment manufacture may be very old indeed: the manufacture of lead white, for example, had been known from Roman times. Small instruction manuals, drawing on the same tradition as the more general 'secrets' books, but usually restricted in their content to a particular craft or group of crafts, such as dyeing or metallurgy, had quite a wide circulation in Northern Europe in the early sixteenth century. An example from the Southern Netherlands, known as the '*Traktaat om kleuren te bereiden*' ('Treatise on the preparation of colours'; Antwerp, Plantin-Moretus Museum MS 253) contains some recipes (such as that for the preparation of lead-tin yellow) that would still have been relevant, if not current, in the first decades of the seventeenth century.[31] To this craft-based and popular technical literature, one may add the more scientific literature, including the European pharmacopoeias and other medical, chemical and botanical literature.

Interest in the more theoretical aspects of painting and the development of the intellectual role of the painter may explain why books on the technique and history of painting were published in Italy long before they appeared elsewhere in Europe. Topics such as perspective, proportions and colour theory, and often the practice of painting, were discussed and some books containing a fair amount of practical information were still influential in the seventeenth century. These included Lomazzo's treatise and Giovanni Battista Armenini's *De' veri precetti della pittura* (Ravenna 1587).

Although the craft-based tradition in which painting developed did not encourage the development of a literature of practical painting, there was a well-developed amateur interest in miniature painting in England by the last quarter of the sixteenth century. *A very proper treatise wherein is briefly sett forthe the arte of Limming* (London 1573) was the earliest English printed instruction manual on painting and similar books were published in Europe, some of which, like Valentin Boltz von Rufach's *Illuminierbuch* (Basel 1549), were quite sophisticated. Early seventeenth-century published literature on oil painting in England arose from much the same tradition: the gentleman-amateur painting as a pastime. The earliest discussion of oil painting is that of Henry Peacham in *The Compleat Gentleman* (London 1622), a book that, like his earlier work *The Art of Drawing with the Pen*, was designed to be educational.[32] An almost contemporary French example, *Essay des merveilles de nature, et des plus nobles artifices* (Rouen 1621), was published by a Jesuit priest, Etienne Binet, under the pseudonym of René François.[33] This book as a whole is very much broader in scope and more varied in its content than Peacham's; one chapter is dedicated to painting. Peacham's discussion is clearly organised and easier for the amateur to follow than Binet's: he describes how to prepare the panel; how to grind the colours and lay them on the palette; the stages in painting the portrait and the representation of various fabrics and landscapes; finally he describes how to clean the brushes, the slab and the muller, and the storage of unused colour under water. In Binet's discussion the actual process of painting is not clearly described, but the book ran into many editions so must have been both popular and widely available. It formed the basis of a manuscript entitled *Recueil des essaies des merveilles de la peinture*, written in 1635, probably in Paris, by Pierre Lebrun, known after its publication by Mrs Merrifield in 1849 as the Brussels manuscript.[34]

Cornelis Pietersz. Biens's *De Teecken-Const* (Amsterdam 1636), which drew heavily on Karel van Mander's *Het Schilder-Boeck* (Haarlem 1604), Gerard ter Brugge's *Verlichtery Kunst-boeck* (Amsterdam 1616), a well-known manual on watercolour painting, and other texts, also contains practical information which must have been gained from artist friends. His discussion of the making of a lay figure has no precedent and the brief details included on pigments used in oil are typical of earlier seventeenth-century practice in the North and South Netherlands.[35] No equivalent text intended for amateur painters or students seems to have been published in the Spanish Netherlands.

One of the most valuable contemporary sources

Fig. 2 Peter Paul Rubens, *Portrait of Theodore Turquet de Mayerne*, c.1630. Canvas, 137 × 109 cm. Raleigh, North Carolina Museum of Art (no. 128).

is the so-called de Mayerne manuscript, *Pictoria, Sculptoria, Tinctoria et quae subalternarum artium spectantia* (British Library MS Sloane 2052).[36] Sir Theodore de Mayerne was a Huguenot refugee, born in Geneva but settled in France, who practised as a physician at the court of James I and, subsequently, Charles I. As well as his medical practice, he was greatly interested in the materials and methods of painting. His position at court (to say nothing of his circle of friends, neighbours and patients) gave him access to both visiting and local artists, including Paul van Somer, Cornelius Johnson, Daniel Mytens, John Hoskins, Rubens, Van Dyck and many others. Edward Norgate was a friend and wrote the first version of his much-copied treatise on illumination in 1627–8 at de Mayerne's request.[37] Rubens, Hoskins and the French illuminator and enamellist Jean Petitot painted his portrait (Fig. 2). He was able to discuss their methods of painting with them, to ask questions, to make suggestions and record the conversations. He also read widely, copying out recipes from these sources, and recorded the results of his experiments.

Where he recorded the concerns of artists or copied down information that plainly relates to current practice, de Mayerne's notes are of special interest. He records pigment prices; the length of time

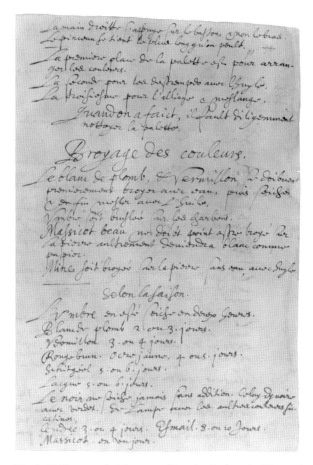

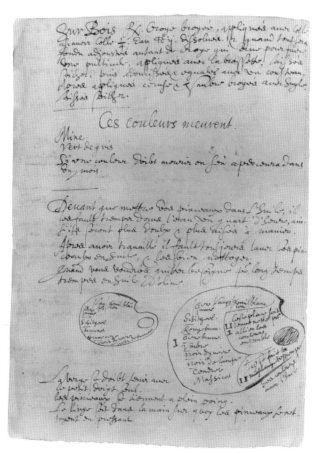

Fig. 3 T. Turquet de Mayerne, *Pictoria, Sculptoria, Tinctoria et quae subalternarum artium spectantia...*, 1620–46. British Library MS Sloane 2052, f. 91ʳ. Drying times for pigments in oil.

Fig. 4 T. Turquet de Mayerne, *Pictoria, Sculptoria, Tinctoria et quae subalternarum artium spectantia...*, 1620–46. British Library MS Sloane 2052, f. 90ᵛ. Diagram showing how pigments should be set out on the palette.

taken for pigments to dry (Fig. 3); their properties; mixtures for different purposes; how to purify oil and prepare drying oils; how the colours could be laid out on the palette (Fig. 4); innumerable varnish recipes and a great deal of random information. His own experimental work, such as that on amber and varnishes, does not necessarily bear any relation to actual artistic practice. However, it cannot be assumed that all the information he gathered during his researches (and some of his sources, like the *Secreti* of Alessio Piemontese, derived from older literature still) was still current in his time. The manuscript was compiled in London, but many of the artists he met were Flemish or French; some, like Rubens, did not stay long. It must be borne in mind, therefore, that materials that concerned them may not have been available locally.

The information in Norgate's manuscript on miniature painting was disseminated by means of manuscript copies through a closely knit circle of gentlemen-amateurs. It also found its way into print,

in an imperfect form, in William Sanderson's *Graphice* (London 1658) and subsequently in the other artists' manuals which appeared from the 1660s onwards, long after Norgate's death. One of the manuscript copies of the first version, British Library MS Harley 6376, written some time after 1641, also contains a section entitled *The Art of Painting in Oyle by the Life*, appended to that on miniature painting.[38] Some of the content, such as the descriptions of containers for cleaning and storing brushes, may derive from the author's own experience or from another unidentified source.[39] By 1679 the manuscript was owned by the York glass-painter Henry Gyles, who added recipes of his own which are very different in content and concept to the earlier sections.

Artists' own writings may also contain useful information on technique, or their attitude to painting. Rubens comments more than once on the drying of paint and he clearly knew that keeping a freshly painted oil painting in the dark would cause it to yellow and that this could be reversed by exposing it to light.[40] Van Dyck's name is associated with several documents. The most important of these is a document in the commonplace book of the Oxford scholar and philologist Dr Thomas Marshall (Oxford, Bodleian Library, MS Marshall 80), headed '*Observat d. Ant … Dykii*'.[41] In this Van Dyck commented briefly on the soundness of technique of *water-verw schilders* (those trained in the use of a water-based paint medium: 'tempera' in its broadest sense) who maintained the disciplined approach of that method in their oil-painting practice. In the seventeenth century a water-based paint (perhaps containing glue size or gum) would be used for tapestry cartoons and decorative projects of all sorts as well as, for example, personal landscape sketches in watercolour. The method is unforgiving in that it does not permit much in the way of alteration. Van Dyck clearly thought this good practice and developed the argument further. He maintained that forms should be sketched in such a way that there was no need to alter them at a later stage (Plate 5). In the first stage of painting, the underpaint stage termed the *maniera lavata*, lean colours should be used so that they dried with a light tone, using a similar colour for the underpaint as that intended for the final layers and paying some attention to the tonal values necessary for the composition. This was to be followed by the modelling of forms, the *maniera sbozzata*, which was supposed to give the work its final form, seemingly by means of modulating the darker areas rather than by the application of highlights. In the last stage, the *maniera finita*, the deepest shadows were applied by glazing; significantly, he drew attention to the work of Titian and other Venetian painters in this context. He also commented on the need for a correct and assured drawing technique. The procedure described is one of sound painting practice and the survey of Van Dyck's paintings in the Collection has confirmed the essential soundness of his technique, the sureness of delineation of his forms and the execution of the composition, once it reached the painting stage. It was, however, backed up by a great facility in drawing and the use of many compositional sketches and drawings where necessary; the work was done before the painting was commenced.

Throughout his Italian travels, Van Dyck noted down the colours of particular elements of the paintings he sketched; these were frequently fabrics and draperies. In his sketch of Titian's *Portrait of Pope Paul III Farnese with his Nephews Alessandro and Ottavio* (Naples, Gallerie Nazionali di

Plate 5 Anthony van Dyck, *A Soldier on Horseback*, *c.*1615–16. Canvas, 91 × 55 cm. Oxford, Christ Church Picture Gallery (no. 246). Oil sketch study for *The Martyrdom of Saint Sebastian c.*1615 (Paris, Musée du Louvre). The composition has been brushed in without alterations using a dark paint; the heads were worked up further in a creamy-white paint.

Capodimonte, then in the Farnese Collection in Rome), for example, the golden colour of the curtain billowing over the heads of the Pope and his sycophantic nephew Ottavio is noted.[42]

On the final leaf of the sketchbook, Van Dyck noted down common ingredients for varnishes, including oil of turpentine, '*aqua di rasa*', fir balsam (from *Abies alba*), '*olio da abezzo*', and pine resin or colophony, '*rasa da pino*', together with unspecified '*vernizia*' and amber varnish. A larger collection of technical recipes is found in another document associated with Van Dyck, the so-called Antwerp sketchbook (Devonshire collection, Chatsworth). It is thought that this in part records a book of drawings from Rubens's studio, now lost, and the attribution

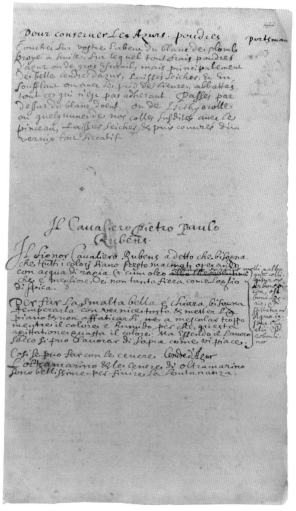

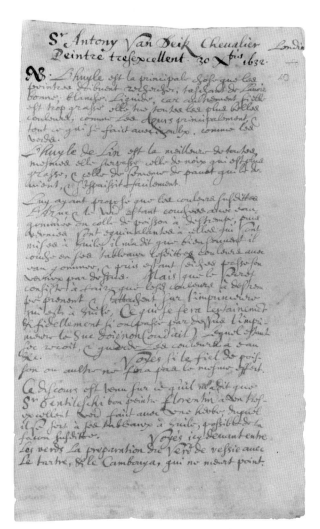

Fig. 5 T. Turquet de Mayerne, *Pictoria, Sculptoria, Tinctoria et quae subalternarum artium spectantia...*, 1620–46. British Library MS Sloane 2052, f. 150ʳ. Remarks by Rubens on grinding pigments and on blues.

Fig. 6 T. Turquet de Mayerne, *Pictoria, Sculptoria, Tinctoria et quae subalternarum artium spectantia...*, 1620–46. British Library MS Sloane 2052, f. 153ʳ. Remarks by Van Dyck on linseed oil and the medium for blues and greens.

to Van Dyck has been much discussed.[43] The written material begins with a rather garbled account of the purification of linseed oil with water, followed by the preparation of drying linseed oil. Mistakenly, the recipe starts from the pressed oil seed, rather than the oil, which would be unlikely in practice. 'Fat' oil is prepared by boiling it with leeks; other contemporary accounts refer to the use of onion, but this is to purify the oil, rather than to body it, so the purpose of the recipe may have been misunderstood. A later recipe for improving the drying properties of oil and bleaching it by standing it in the sun appears to have been quite standard; it is one that de Mayerne also recorded from his informants.[44] Other recipes include one for turpentine varnish (presumably using pine resin, although this is not stated); an ink from which copies could be taken; an etching ground; and

preparations for refined (recrystallised) verdigris and an artificial copper-containing blue or blue green pigment from copper filings, nitric acid and chalk or white lead. At the end of the collection it is noted that Strasbourg turpentine (fir balsam) makes a very good varnish, the Venetian turpentine (larch resin) being unsuitable. In practice this is true; fir balsam produces a very much more resilient film and was recommended for uses where resilience or water-proofing was required.[45] Many of the individual instructions can be paralleled by recipes in other collections. The fact that some are misunderstood, or mistranscribed, suggests that there was an interest in the technology of contemporary materials and processes within the circle of Rubens and Van Dyck, but that the transcriber did not always have quite the technical understanding to record them accurately.

Remarks attributed to Rubens and Van Dyck recorded by de Mayerne were often of general concern. Rubens, for example, told de Mayerne that pigments should be ground quickly working with turpentine, which was better and less fierce than oil of spike lavender (this would be the preliminary grinding, before grinding with the oil medium) (Fig. 5). He also recommended dipping the brush in turpentine occasionally before blending the colours on the palette so that the paint was more easily worked and the colours did not 'die', or sink, 'as for blues'. Blue pigments seem to have been perceived as a particular problem, partly because of their handling properties in oil and their tendency to sink, but also because of the danger that they would yellow.[46] In conversation with Van Dyck, de Mayerne suggested that he might do well to use an aqueous medium for his blues and greens, then to varnish them, the problem being to apply the tempera-based colours over the oil paint beneath without their flaking off; Van Dyck apparently agreed that he had tried this.[47] It must be said, however, that where it was possible to examine passages of blue or green paint in Van Dyck's paintings in the Collection, no evidence was found for the use of anything other than oil (see pp. 84–8). Van Dyck shared the rather common concern about the quality of his oil (Fig. 6); it should be good, pale and liquid and if it was too *grasse* (fat, that is, prepolymerised and so thickened, and with improved drying qualities) it killed the other colours, particularly the blues (presumably it was darker in colour).

The notes de Mayerne made in conversation with Rubens and Van Dyck can be added to the comments made by painters, and others, who had known or worked with them in the past. Van Dyck's working habits were observed by those who had worked in his studio, such as the painter James Gandy. It is thought that a collection of notes copied by the eighteenth-century painter Ozias Humphreys was perhaps made by James's son William, based on his father's recollections and those of others who had known the painter. From these, and similar notes, it is possible to learn (from Gandy's conversation with Richard Gibson) that, in drawing a sketch for a portrait, Van Dyck drew freely on blue paper in black chalk, heightened with white. He also stored his paints under water, except for the red and yellow lakes, Cologne (or Cassel) earth and indigo, and bought oil of turpentine and mastic.[48] From such small snippets of information some picture of his studio practice may be constructed.

Contemporary biographies may contain small, but sometimes quite revealing, pieces of information on an artist's technique; they may also conflict with other accounts. Bellori's account of Van Dyck's life states that he was in the habit of working through without a break, beginning his portraits in the morning and perhaps keeping his sitters over lunch.[49] As it is thought that Bellori may have received some of his information from Van Dyck's friend Sir Kenelm Digby, whose portrait Van Dyck painted, one might suppose it to be accurate. On the other hand, Roger de Piles, recording the experiences of the Paris art-collector Everhard Jabach, who sat to the painter three times, describes a very different system, whereby the painter worked on the portrait for an hour only, making another appointment when the time was up, then being brought a fresh palette and clean brush for the next sitter. Assistants painted the clothing up to the final stage from Van Dyck's sketch and the artist applied the finishing touches.[50] Perhaps both were accurate in describing his practice in their experience; a close friend, for example, might have received a different treatment from that accorded to a patron.

Studios

Contemporary accounts of the requirements for the painter's studio, such as those of the German painter and writer Joachim von Sandrart, or the author of *The Art of Painting in Oyle by the Life* (MS Harley 6376), concentrate on two points: the size of the room and the lighting. Sandrart drew attention to the need for space and suggested the room should be about thirty feet square; according to the author of the manuscript, the model should be four to six yards away from the painter. Rubens's studio was lit from above, but usually a north-facing window, giving constant, cool light, was recommended, with blinds or curtains to control the amount of light entering the room and the amount of shadow: 'sometimes it is requisite that your pictures have but little shadowes, yt [that] sometimes ye painter must please ye female sex, for they will not be painted with deep shadowes.'[51]

Literary sources also describe the equipment necessary: easels, strainers, grinding stones of porphyry or some other stone and mullers to prepare the paint, palettes, brushes, knives and a mahlstick (Fig. 7).[52] It has been pointed out that, while there is no problem in the identification of the larger, hog's bristle brushes, the hair used for the soft hair brushes or 'pensills' is not always easy to identify: the English word 'fitch', for example, means polecat, a member

Fig. 7 Gonzalez Coques, *The Artist's Studio*, c.1665. Oil on canvas laid down on panel, 65 × 81.5 cm. Schwerin, Staatliches Museum (no. 171). The canvas on the easel has been laced into a temporary stretching frame. A mahlstick, used as an arm support during painting, leans against the table to the left. In the foreground is a paint box.

of the same family as the weasel and the ermine. Hair from the tails of these species was used for brushmaking. However, 'fitch' also referred to a square-ended brush and this is the more likely interpretation. The hairs were inserted into quills of different sizes, from the feathers of water fowl such as geese, ducks or swans, and a handle of wood or some other material was inserted into the other end.[53] The inventory of the goods of the Antwerp painter Adriaen Brouwer, taken on 5 October 1632, includes eighteen brushes – '*pinceelen*'– with sticks as well as ten brush sticks, or handles, on their own and three dozen brushes, either without handles or where none is mentioned. Following the brushes, a 'wooden manikin with its stand' is listed, conceivably a lay figure.[54] The frontispiece of John Bate's book illustrates a painter at work, showing the easel and other items of equipment; the author of MS Harley 6376 drew a diagram of a portable easel. As mentioned above, he also drew the containers for brush cleaning and storage made of 'latten' (probably tin-plated iron rather than brass in this case).[55]

Inventories of artists' property give much information on the more valuable contents of artists' studios. Almost all list easels and grinding stones, which must have been of some value.[56] In the studio of Jan Snellinck the Elder was a grinding stone, two

easels, two palettes, three stools, a small cupboard or set of shelves for colours and another smaller grinding stone. Another room contained a few frames and strainers and a chest of drawings.[57] The studio of Joos de Momper contained three easels, paintings in various stages of completion, five palettes, three stools and a collection of brushes, oil and unspecified pigments.[58] Pigments could be kept in glasses, shells or pots, or indeed, in the form of dry pigment, wrapped in paper; these could be stored in wooden chests.[59] The inventory of the property of Margriet Briers, the widow of Hendrik van Balen the Elder, who died on 23 October 1638, six years after her husband, included a number of easels and a large grinding slab on a trestle, and a collection of sculptures. Among these were figures from Graeco-Roman mythology, plaster casts of busts, hands and feet, a stone figure described as an *Anothomi*, another in plaster ascribed to 'Jan de Boloni' (Giambologna, presumably) and yet another made of red wax in a wooden case.[60] The painter Steven Wils the Younger owned a similar range of sculpture and a large collection of drawings and engravings, both bound and unbound.[61] This was not unusual: many, perhaps most, artists had collections of prints and drawings for reference, although some at least would have been of their own making.

The studio played an essential role in the fulfilment of commissions and in any production of pieces for speculative sales, rather as the large successful workshops of fifteenth- and sixteenth-century painters like Robert Campin or Rogier van der Weyden had earlier: the painter as entrepreneur and the studio as a commercial enterprise were not new. Painters also specialised in particular types of painting and often collaborated: a specialist in landscapes or still-life scenes might be brought in. Frans Snijders, for example, who painted still lifes and animal scenes, is known to have collaborated with Rubens and other figure painters.[62] The Rubens studio, its structure and how far Rubens himself intervened in any particular painting has been the subject of much discussion and analysis (and see pp. 96–104 in this *Bulletin).*[63] The account of Van Dyck's portrait painting practice given by Everhard Jabach to Roger de Piles describes a studio production system very well: the master retained the intellectual responsibility for any product of the studio as he conceived and produced the original design, although the overall quality of the final product depended on the extent of his intervention.[64] Van Dyck's work for the English court often involved the production of portraits in different versions and inevitably there were variations in the quality, especially in some of the later portraits.[65] The responsibility for the quality of the product, however, rested with the master. There is evidence that Rubens, for example, corrected details on paintings that were primarily studio productions; clearly he could not ignore the possible implications of what might be seen as substandard.[66]

Supports

Although both canvas and wood panels were used as supports for casel painting in the earlier part of the seventeenth century, the use of canvas became far more common as time went on. In Italy the majority of easel paintings were on canvas, even at the beginning of the century. In Northern Europe generally, where there was a greater availability of suitable timber, panels were more widely used, particularly for smaller works, but even here there was a decline in the use of wood supports after the first half of the century. The smooth, even surface of panel, which would permit meticulous, detailed work and a flawless finish if so desired, was undoubtedly appealing to some painters and patrons; this may be one reason behind the relative popularity of metal panels as a support at this time. The slightly grainy texture of canvas is suited to a looser, freer style of painting; precision equivalent to that achieved on smooth supports cannot be obtained on even the most closely woven, finely grounded canvas. Rubens thought that panels were in any case more suitable for small works and consistently used them for preliminary studies, a practice Van Dyck seems to have followed to some extent.[67] Most of Rubens's landscapes, which show a high degree of detail and finish, but were essentially for his own pleasure and private use, are on panel. Clearly, paintings of a less intimate nature, such as the cycle of works glorifying the life of Marie de Medici (now in the Musée du Louvre, Paris), were conceived on a larger scale. They were intended to be seen and to make an impact at a distance; the handling is thus appropriately broader.[68]

For commissioned works, the wishes of the patron and the intended site for the picture would play some part in the choice of support. With certain notable exceptions discussed below, canvas was more commonly used for larger works; it was cheaper, lighter and far easier to transport from the painter's studio to the final site, which might be some distance away. For example, the paintings for the ceiling of the Banqueting House in Whitehall, commissioned by Charles I in 1630 at the end of Rubens's brief stay in London on a diplomatic mission, were painted in Antwerp so would have to be rolled, packed and transported by sea. In his letters Rubens referred several times to the packing and transport of pictures and, by this time, such movements would have been in no way unusual.[69]

Panel

The wood used for panels in both the northern and southern parts of the Netherlands and in England at this time appears to have been oak, almost exclusively.[70] Dendrochronological evidence indicates that, from the fifteenth century or earlier until about 1650, this was imported, principally from the eastern Baltic regions, generally in the form of boards or planks.[71] In contemporary documents, the Dutch *wagenschot* and English 'wainscot' appear generally to refer to oak boards or planks (quarter-sawn or cleaved), rather than to beams or other pieces of greater thickness (Fig. 8). The 1560 trading book of the Münster merchant Jakob Stöve, who dealt in Gdansk (Danzig) timber, describes how this grade of wood should be fine, free of knots and heartwood and without cracks or spiral-grained wood.[72] Gdansk, in present-day Poland, was the principal exporting centre for this timber; the town was on the edge of vast forests, the source of a limitless supply of well-

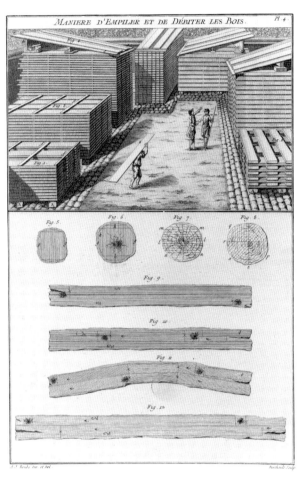

Fig. 8 Sawing logs into planks: the different cuts obtained. A.-J. Roubo, *L'Art de menuisier*, Paris 1769–75, plate 4, 'Manière d'empiler et de débiter les bois'. London, British Library.

grown, similarly sized trees. Much of the Baltic trade, including that in Gdansk timber, was with the Northern Netherlands: most of it reached Antwerp by way of Amsterdam. During the late sixteenth and the seventeenth centuries the Gdansk trade was affected by outbreaks of war, although as wood was exported from Gdansk to Spain between 1607–18, supplies in the Spanish Netherlands may not have been much affected at this time.[73] The blockade of Gdansk harbour during the war between Sweden and Poland from 1626 to1629 provoked a more serious disruption; trade was finally brought to a complete standstill by a second Swedish-Polish war from 1650 to 1655.[74]

Beams derived from this oak were on average between ten and fourteen feet long. It seems that, in seventeenth-century Antwerp, the longest available oak planks measured about twelve feet, around 344 cm (converting from the Antwerp foot of 28.68 cm).[75] The problems this caused are shown, for example, in two of six massive altarpieces painted by Rubens for

Antwerp churches between 1610 and 1625; both are triptychs. The painted surface of the central panel of the earliest of these, the *Elevation of the Cross*, painted in 1610–11, measures 459.5 cm by 339.6 cm. In the second, the *Descent from the Cross*, painted for the Cathedral in 1611–14, the painted surface of the central panel measures 417 cm by 307 cm approximately. The remaining four altarpieces are single panels, but, following the Italian model developed during the previous century, are very tall: the latest, and tallest, the *Assumption of the Virgin*, painted for the Cathedral in 1625–6, is approximately 490 cm high and 325 cm wide. (It was made wider even before any painting was carried out in 1624; this is discussed below.) The other three, the *Last Communion of Saint Francis* (1618), the *Coup de Lance* (1620) and the *Adoration of the Magi* (1624), all now in the Koninklijk Museum voor Schone Kunsten, Antwerp, have heights of between 420 and 450 cm.[76] In every case, the panel – or central panel in the case of the triptychs – has been constructed using planks running horizontally rather than vertically: nineteen planks in the case of the *Elevation of the Cross* (of which the bottom one is not original) and seventeen in the *Descent from the Cross*. Aligning the planks parallel to the longest dimension was the usual construction method; this gives a stronger, more stable structure and entails fewer joints.

The structural difficulties faced are particularly apparent in the construction of the wings of the two triptychs. In the *Elevation of the Cross*, the left wing consists of six horizontal planks surmounted by six vertical to give the required height, while in the right wing this is reversed: the six vertical planks, 313.5 cm long, are topped by six horizontal planks (the painted surface of the wings is 150 cm wide). The two sets of planks are joined by a V-shaped tongue-and-groove joint (the groove being inserted into the ends of the vertical planks); otherwise open butt joints, reinforced by dowels, have been used throughout the construction. The panels are in good condition, except in the area of the joint between the vertical and horizontal planks; this inherently unstable piece of construction must have been necessary because planks of sufficient length (about 460 cm) were unobtainable. The longest planks in the altarpiece are those in the main panel (about 340 cm, or a little under twelve Antwerp feet) and in none of these six large altarpieces were the planks longer than 350 cm.[77] In the *Descent from the Cross*, a similar construction was used for the wings, but this time the V-shaped joint was placed high up in both wings, where it would be less obvious to the viewer and structurally rather more secure.[78] It is interesting in this context that, in April 1613, the deacon and council of the Kolveniers Guild in Antwerp, who had commissioned the *Descent*, went with a joiner to St Walburga to examine the *Elevation* panel for possible faults; the panel-maker was Hans van Haecht in both cases. Conceivably this had some bearing on the orientation of the wing panels.[79]

Although wood was the traditional support for altarpieces, it was not invariably used. The three altarpieces Rubens painted in 1628 for the church of St Augustine, Antwerp (at present in the Koninklijk Museum voor Schone Kunsten) are all on canvas.[80] The choice and commissioning of the support was often the business of the client, rather than the artist. This is clearly shown by the documents for the *Elevation of the Cross*, and can be seen in the case of an altarpiece depicting the *Last Supper* for the abbey church of Sint-Winocksbergen (Bergues-Saint-Winoc) at Dunkerque, commissioned in 1611.[81] An even clearer example is the triptych of the *Miraculous Draught of Fishes*, painted by Rubens in 1618 for the Fishmongers' Guild at the church of Onze-Lieve-Vrouw-over-de-Dyle, Mechelen. The panel for this had been commissioned in 1614 and was in position on the altar, ready to be painted, the following year, but Rubens did not visit Mechelen to see the site until October 1617 and the contract was not finalised until February 1618.[82] Less is known about private commissions.

Panel-makers were registered in the Guild of Saint Luke, like the painters. In 1617, articles controlling the inspection and marking of panels and frames were incorporated in the regulations and also into those of the Schrijnwerkers (Joiners), in order that they should cover all those who were likely to supply goods of this kind. From these it is possible to learn that joined panels, large and small, were supposed to be made of dry – that is, seasoned – wood, without areas of sapwood or other weakness, fire damage or woodworm. The use of good '*wageschot*' rather than beech or softwood was required for large frames and so forth. Any panel-maker attempting to sell a panel before it had been inspected and branded by the Dean of the Guild or one of the inspectors (*keurmeesters*) was subject to a substantial fine (twelve guilders a panel) and if the wood was poor or the panel was in some other way not up to standard the inspecting officer was empowered to break it.[83] In practice the inspection was not always quite so rigorous.[84]

The inventory of the estate of Antonette Wiael,

Fig. 9 The joiner's workshop, showing a saw, an axe, planes and other tools. Hans Sachs, *Eygentliche Beschreibung aller Stände auff Erden*, with illustrations by Jost Amman, Frankfurt-am-Main 1568, f. Z.iv, 'Der Schreiner'. London, British Library.

widow of the panel-maker Hans van Haecht, made on 5–7 July 1627, provides an insight into the panel-maker's trade. Van Haecht himself had died six years before, in 1621. Among the contents of the cellar or basement of the house '*de Coninck van Vranckryk*' in the Lombardenvest, Antwerp, were three carpenter's benches, wood suitable for joinery ('*schrynwerckershout*'), faulty panels to be remade or to be used as a source of wood, an iron glue kettle, a copper glue pot, joiner's cramps and a selection of tools, including an axe, shears (or knives), four saws, pliers, pincers, two drills, grinding- or whetstones and unspecified joiner's tools (Fig. 9). There were also unfinished frames and 148 eight-stuiver-sized panels, some still in the cramps used to hold the boards in place while the glue in the joints hardened. The inventory also records the presence of primed and unprimed ('*rou*') panels, in a variety of sizes and formats, and different types of frame in other parts of the property.[85]

From early in the century, the panel-maker was also responsible for having the white ground of chalk mixed with animal-skin glue applied to the panel;

this he might do himself or he might employ a *witter* (whitener), but the ground could not be applied until after the inspection.[86] In some cases the client commissioning the work paid an artist to prime the panel before the principal artist started work; however, it is not necessarily clear whether this meant simply the application of the ground, or of a thin layer of paint tinting its surface and also acting as an isolating layer (discussed below), or both. In 1625, for example, Adriaen Schut (registered in the *Liggeren* of the Guild of Saint Luke as a painter) was paid eight guilders to prime the panel for the *Assumption of the Virgin* and to paint its frame black before Rubens started work on it.[87] Ground could be applied to the back of the panel as well as to the front. It was a long-established practice to paint the back; it is seen in many fifteenth- and sixteenth-century Netherlandish panels and has the effect of protecting the wood from changes in relative humidity, thus reducing its tendency to swell, shrink or warp. The Van Haecht/Wiael inventory includes panels described as primed on both sides.[88] Examples in the National Gallery Collection include Rubens's *Minerva and Mercury conduct the Duke of Buckingham to the Temple of Virtue* (Plate 8, p. 29), painted before 1625, and *The Rape of the Sabine Women* (NG 38), painted

Fig. 10 Peter Paul Rubens, *The Coup de Lance* (NG 1865), before 1620. Oak, 64.8 × 49.9 cm.

around 1635–40. As mentioned above, movement of the wood is a particular problem for panels with structural members aligned both vertically and horizontally; the presence of a coating on the panel reverse might thus be expected. It is found, for example, on Rubens's *An Autumn Landscape with a View of Het Steen in the Early Morning* (NG 66), which is painted on a panel constructed of some nineteen planks (another two were added later) arranged horizontally and vertically.[89]

In 1617 a regulation was introduced to control the number of standard sizes of panels, which from this time were to be based on models kept in the Guild office.[90] The regulation lists five sizes, from a guilder to a half-stooter (a stooter was equivalent to 2.5 stuivers), but in practice other sizes, such as sixteen stuivers, also occur, which are not listed. The fact that some of the Van Haecht/Wiael panels were described as 'long' or 'large' versions suggests also that neither the size nor the format requirements were inflexible. An attempt has been made to link the named sizes with actual measurements, based on the identification of existing paintings with those listed in inventories; this and more recent work suggest that another unlisted size, the *salvator*, measuring about 60 × 50 cm, was very widely used. The panel Rubens used for *The Coup de Lance* (NG 1865, Fig. 10), the sketch for the altarpiece for the church of the Récollets, is approximately this size (64.8 × 49.9 cm). That used by Van Dyck for *Carlo and Ubaldo see Rinaldo conquered by Love for Armida* (NG 877.2), a sketch for an engraving painted 1634–5, is a little narrow, measuring 57 × 41.5 cm, but both panels were branded on the reverse with the mark of the city of Antwerp and the latter also bears the initials of the panel-maker Michiel Vriendt. The twenty-six-stuiver size appears to measure about 75 × 110 cm.[91] This is very close to the size of the panel used by Rubens for *A Lion Hunt* (NG 853.1) painted around 1616–17, which measures 73.6 × 105.4 cm and is marked on the reverse.

Antwerp panel marks have been the subject of much study. The 1617 regulations stipulated that no panel could be sold or primed until it had been inspected and branded by the Dean of the Guild or his representative. This brand took the form of a castle and a pair of hands representing the city of Antwerp; different branding irons were used over the years (sometimes concurrently) and their design varied in detail.[92] The 1617 regulations further stipulated that the panel (or frame) should be marked by its maker's personal mark; the penalty for not so

Plate 6 Peter Paul Rubens, *Portrait of Susanna Lunden (?)* ('*Le Chapeau de Paille*') (NG 852), probably 1622–3. Oak, 79 × 54.6 cm.

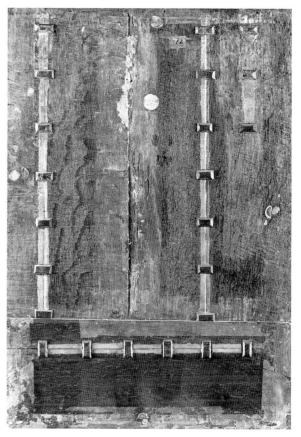

Fig. 11 Peter Paul Rubens, *Portrait of Susanna Lunden (?)*. Reverse (with later reinforcement). The original panel of two planks was extended during painting with a narrow strip seen on the left, and at the bottom by a plank with the grain running horizontally.

doing was a fine of three guilders. At this time, twenty-one panel-makers registered their marks.[93] A great many marked panels have been found and many of the panel-makers have been identified. Michiel Vriendt's mark 'MV' is found on several panels in the Collection: apart from those mentioned above it also appears on the reverse of Rubens's *Portrait of Susanna Lunden* (NG 852, probably painted 1622–3, Plate 6), and on David Teniers's *Two Men playing Cards in the Kitchen of an Inn* (NG 2600, probably 1635–40). A painting attributed to Teniers, *Peasants making Music in an Inn* (NG 154, about 1635) is marked F/ DB, the mark of the panel-maker Franchois De Bont (François de Bout).

If panel-making was so strictly controlled the question arises as to how certain panels could have been passed as satisfactory by the Guild when their construction was unsound. Many of these are associated with Rubens and with his landscapes in particular. As explained earlier, these were not commissioned, but were entirely private works, and

it could be said that they constitute a special case. As a court artist Rubens was himself a special case: he was not obliged to register his apprentices with the Guild and perhaps his position may have given him other exemptions also, so that when he had panels made up for his own use at his own expense, he could have them made as economically as possible. However, there are other possible interpretations and in one or two cases, such as *Sunset Landscape with a Shepherd and his Flock* (NG 2924) and '*The Watering Place*' (NG 4815), both painted around 1615–22, it is possible that the artist reworked and extended a pre-existing composition.[94]

Additions to a pre-existing support contemporary with the painting process are not uncommon and may have been carried out for a number of reasons. The support, or the finished painting even, might turn out to be the wrong size for the site, or the intended site might be changed. When the panel for the *Assumption of the Virgin* was set up on the high altar in Antwerp Cathedral in 1624 it was found to be too narrow and had to be enlarged, a task for which Michiel Vriendt was paid thirty-eight guilders in 1625.[95] Several of the surviving canvases for the Torre de la Parada hunting lodge, commissioned by Philip IV around 1636 and painted, following oil sketches by Rubens, by Rubens himself and other Antwerp artists, have been enlarged and it seems likely they were made to the wrong dimensions for their intended positions.[96] Another difficulty, referred to by Rubens in his letters, was that units of measurement varied from place to place; allowance was usually made for this, but not always successfully.[97] Sometimes additions were made for reasons of economy: a pre-existing, unused support was enlarged. This may partly explain the additions to the panel Rubens used for *The Three Graces* (Madrid, Museo del Prado). The central portion consists of a panel of six vertical planks, of high quality, bearing the Antwerp brand. An addition was then made on the left-hand side; then a section made up of short, vertically aligned planks, slightly narrower than those used for the original panel, was attached at the top with a half-lap joint and glue. (Examination of Rubens's landscape panels has shown that this joint was frequently used to make additions to a pre-existing panel.[98]) Finally a full-length addition was made on the right. However, there is another possibility: as the figures fit the original portion exactly, it could be that the artist decided to add to the composition during painting, as he did in the *Portrait of Susanna Lunden* (Fig. 11).

Canvas

Canvases in both twill and plain tabby weaves, woven in various widths and different degrees of coarseness, are found across Europe. Probably most are linen, although hemp fibres could also be used, particularly for coarser fabrics; hemp was apparently used in the Dutch sailcloth industry, for example.[99] As most seventeenth-century canvas paintings have been lined it is rarely possible to investigate the fibres of the original canvas itself. Twill-weave fabrics are more easily characterised, although rather rarely used; ticking is an example (discussed below). The important factors, as far as the quality of the fabric was concerned, were that it should be strong, usually relatively closely and evenly woven and with few knots.

In the Low Countries and many other Northern European countries, cloth was measured by the ell and woven to a range of standard widths based on this measure, expressed by such terms as 'six quarters', 6/4 ells, and so on. The precise dimensions of the ell varied from place to place, although the ell of Brabant, equivalent to about 69.6 cm and used in both Antwerp and Brussels, was widely used for trading purposes. Thus, for the Brabant ell, the 6/4 width would be equivalent to 104.4 cm and the 5/4 width to about 87 cm. In England the yard measure, first standardised according to an iron measuring rod during the reign of Richard I in 1196, predated the ell, and cloth widths (expressed as above, but as fractions of a yard) were based on this. The ell, 5/4 yards or 45 inches (about 114 cm), was in use by the fourteenth century, but seems not to have been defined by a standard (bronze) measure until 1588.[100] According to Lewis Roberts, in *The Merchants Mappe of Commerce* (London 1638), wool and silk were commonly measured by the yard in the City of London, while the ell was used for linen; 60 ells of London were equivalent to 100 Antwerp ells (understandably, his conversion factors are based on large quantities of goods).[101] The units of measurement in the Italian states were usually based on the *canna* (cane) or the *braccia*, which were subdivided according to local custom; frequently the subdivisions varied according to what was being measured. In Genoa, according to Roberts, the cane was subdivided into nine palms (equivalent to about 24.8 cm) for silks, but ten for linen; 100 palms were equivalent to 27 yards or about 34 Antwerp ells. The cane measure used for linen was thus equivalent to about 248 cm. In Rome the *braccia mercantile*, consisting of four *palmi da tela* (about 21.2 cm), or the *braccia da tessitore* (*tela*), three *palmi da tela*, might be used.[102]

Although linen was produced around Antwerp and other towns, Ghent was one of the most important centres for the linen industry in the Spanish Netherlands throughout the seventeenth century.[103] All types of linen were produced, from ticking for bedding to fine damask and table linen, and much was exported. After Spain and the Spanish colonies, the most important market was England. Flax was imported from the Baltic region, particularly the region around Riga in present-day Lithuania, and woven in the villages all around Ghent. The linen would then be brought into the city at the Friday Market to be assessed. In the early years of the century, the linen merchants had insisted that, at this stage, the cloth should be measured according to a standard unit, the crude or rough linen ell of about 76.5 cm (30 English inches).[104] The quality of the linen was indicated by seals: *Brabantes* and *Presillas* cloth with the required width of 6/4 ells (about 114.75 cm, by this measure: rather more than the Brabant equivalent would be, but very close to the English ell) was marked with a black lion in 'oil colour'. Pieces that were a little too narrow were marked accordingly. The *Brabantes* was the better quality of the two and was sold in three grades: superfine (exported to Spain), fine and ordinary. *Presillas* was a more workman-like, coarser type of cloth, suitable for sails or trousers, for example, and sold in two grades. The dearest variety of linen, the *Gantes* or Ghents, was sold at the small linen market and, if of the required width of one and a quarter ells (95.6 cm), it was marked with a lead seal in the form of a crowned 'G'. Of the three grades available, the superfine was exported by land to southern Europe; the fine and ordinary went by sea to various parts of Europe, including England.

The English linen industry was small by comparison with the wool industry; much was imported from other parts of Europe, principally France and the Low Countries. Linen and, in particular, canvas for use as sailcloth were imported from Brittany and Normandy: Noyales and Vitry canvas appear in the accounts for the naval dockyards at Chatham in 1629 and 1630.[105] In this context, it is worth noting that Dutch sources mention the use of sailcloth as a support for paintings and Vitry canvas was one of the cloths used for the decorative scheme executed by Hans Holbein and others for Henry VIII at Greenwich in 1527, partly for use on the roof.[106] An indication of the varieties of linens imported may be gained from the 1642 edition of *The Rates of Merchandizes*. The list includes brown (unbleached) and white Dutch, Prussian and French canvas (including Vitry canvas), damask, lawns, calico, towelling, cloths described as Flanders and Holland cloths – Flemish, Ghentish, 'Overisils' (from Overijssel), Brabant, 'Freeze' (from Friesland), brown and bag Holland are examples – dowlas (a coarse linen from Brittany), 'Ozenbrigs' (from Osnabrück), twill and ticking (the last described as from 'the East Country' and from Scotland). The equivalent list of duties on exported goods shows that some canvas, sacking and ticking (woven in twelve-yard lengths, the width not given), was exported from England.[107]

A small handbook for drapers written in 1695 describes many of the fabrics, their widths and the lengths in which they were sold, whether or not they had been bleached or 'whitened', and suggested uses. The French canvases, the import of which was apparently prohibited at that time, were omitted.

Various types of Holland were described. At this time 'Burelaps' (burlap) was one of these: later the name was applied to hemp or jute canvas, used for sacks and bags. It wore well if thick and even-threaded and came in widths of an ell (45 inches), a yard or 3/4 yard (27 inches). Many, including the Ghentish Hollands, came in widths equivalent to the English ell and yard, as can be seen from the discussion of Ghent fabrics above. 'Frize' (Friesland) Holland appeared less evenly woven, thinner and less strong than the others because it had not been calendered or thickened after bleaching, 'but is just as it comes from the whitster'; it was in fact very strong. 'Linnen – Hemp Roles', which was always imported unbleached, was a strong coarse linen a yard (91.4 cm) wide: 'although not very thick, it wears admirable strong; there is much of it used brown for ordinary Painting'. 'Ozenbrucks' (Osnabrück), a coarse linen, was also used unbleached for painting.[108]

Little is documented on the choice of textiles for painting supports in seventeenth-century England and most of our information (relating to the portrait painter Mary Beale and to Sir Peter Lely) dates from some forty years after Van Dyck's death; however, the recurrence of textile names in sources throughout the century suggests that what was chosen in the 1670s and 80s would have been available earlier. Charles Beale, the husband of Mary Beale (1632/3–99), acted as a colourman and also stretched and primed canvases. His pocket books for 1677 and 1681 record the purchase of eight types of cloth as painting supports, including the 'Oznabrug'. Sacking appears to have been quite widely used; it is also referred to in the account book of the executors of the estate of Sir Peter Lely (d. 1680) between 1679 and 1691.[109] Two of Charles Beale's other chosen textiles, flaxen and 'Gentish Holland' are discussed above. Another, 'Dutch cloth', was probably a type of Holland.

Beale's last cloth, ticking, is in one way an unexpected choice for a support as it was often striped dark blue or black (as it is today); yet it is extremely strong and closely woven and available in larger widths. Typically it was used for beds: 'ticks'.[110] Ticking seems to have been used particularly for very large works. It was used for Van Dyck's huge *Equestrian Portrait of Charles I* (NG 1172), painted in 1637–8. The support, which measures 367 cm (144 inches) high and 292.1 cm (115 inches) wide, is made up of two pieces of fabric with a horizontal seam; this gives the width of each piece as at least 72 inches (two yards) wide, and in practice it must have been more to allow for the turnover (see p. 77). One of

Plate 7 Jacob Jordaens, *Portrait of Govaert van Surpele (?) and his Wife* (NG 6293), probably 1636–8. Canvas, 213.3 × 189 cm.

the earliest commissions Van Dyck carried out on his return to England in 1632, the so-called 'Great Peece', the group portrait of *Charles I and Queen Henrietta Maria with their Two Eldest Children, Charles, Prince of Wales, and Mary, Princess Royal* (Collection of Her Majesty The Queen), is also on ticking. The painted surface originally measured 298.1 × 250.8 cm, including additions made by Van Dyck at the top and on the right, but was subsequently enlarged.[111] Larger still was the group portrait of *Philip Herbert, 4th Earl of Pembroke, and his Family* (Salisbury, Wilton House), painted between 1633 and 1637 and measuring 330 × 510 cm (see note 40 on p. 83 of this *Bulletin*).[112] Ticking was not only used in England: it has been identified in three seventeenth-century Flemish paintings, one of which, *The Coronation of the Virgin*, painted between 1636 and 1645 by Nicolas de Liemaker (Ghent, Museum voor Schone Kunsten), at 324 × 241 cm, is almost as large as the *Equestrian Portrait of Charles I*.[113] In each case, the fabric is striped dark blue, the warp threads in the stripes being dyed with indigo.

Clearly, cloth that could be used as a painting support in the Spanish Netherlands, England or anywhere else was available in a range of 'standard' widths, some of which were very much wider than those described above; an example is that used for

The Brazen Serpent (NG 59), painted by Rubens between 1635 and 1640 (186.4 cm high and 264.5 cm wide, lined, edges covered by paper).[114] The inventory of a Rotterdam shop selling artists' materials, made in 1673, lists several widths of artists' canvas imported from Antwerp: 5/4 ells (about 87 cm), 7/4 ells (about 121 cm) and 2 ells (about 139 or 140 cm); other widths were not specified.[115] It seems highly likely that canvas in these widths was available in Antwerp, and perhaps exported elsewhere, earlier in the century. It is also likely that, as far as English paintings are concerned, most cloth would have been imported. However, it would usually be impossible to assign the canvas used for any particular painting to any particular source, as the widths of the different textiles were in practice often rather close and it is difficult to assess the original width of the fabric used for a painting support. As most canvases have been lined and have often lost any trace of their original tacking edges, there is no selvedge upon which to base the measurement and the allowance for the tacking edge must be estimated. Where there is a seam, one selvedge for each piece might be observable, but only if the edges of the pieces had been sewn butted together. One example where remains of the original selvedges could still be observed (during conservation treatment) is David Desgranges's group portrait of *The Saltonstall Family* (London, Tate Gallery), painted around 1636–7.[116]

It is frequently found that canvas supports have been pieced together, using narrower strips and pieces added to one side of a larger piece or pieces to make up the required size. Sometimes such additions indicate later modifications to the composition. Jacob Jordaens's *Portrait of Govaert van Surpele(?) and his Wife* (NG 6293, Plate 7) of about 1636–8, which is on a support made up of six pieces of canvas appears to have been conceived in at least two stages. The strips at the bottom were added by the artist when he needed to alter the composition.[117]

The relative coarseness or fineness of a canvas can be expressed in the form of a thread count, giving a measure of the thread density. When it has been possible to examine Flemish and English plain tabby-weave canvases (generally in the form of their X-radiographs, rather than directly) thread counts have been in the range 11–20 threads/cm, both in the warp and in the weft; the weft threads themselves may be less even in their thickness and (as one might expect from the weaving process) the weft counts in any one canvas may vary more than those of the warp, but only to a very small extent. Most of the

The National Gallery Technical Bulletin

Volumes 1–20 CONTENTS

The National Gallery Technical Bulletin is published by and available from National Gallery Publications.
Volumes 14–20 are distributed by Yale University Press.
*Volumes marked * are out of print.*

canvases used by Rembrandt and other Dutch painters fall into the same range.[118] Several of the paintings Van Dyck produced in England are on canvases of rather similar weights, the portrait of *Lady Elizabeth Thimbelby and Dorothy, Viscountess Andover* (NG 6437, about 1637) is on a canvas with 11 threads in the warp and 11–12 in the weft; that for *Lord John Stuart and his Brother, Lord Bernard Stuart* (NG 6518, about 1638) appears to be of a rather similar grade. The portraits, on single pieces of cloth, are similar in width (149 cm and 146.1 cm respectively), suggesting that the same width of canvas was used for the two. The portrait of *A Lady of the Spencer Family* (London, Tate Gallery), painted around 1633–8, is on a very similar canvas, 11 threads in the warp, about 13 in the weft.[119] It seems that this particular grade was quite popular; certainly it was not unique to Van Dyck: Cornelis Jonson's *Portrait of an Unknown Lady* (London, Tate Gallery, 1646), for example, was painted on a canvas with 11 threads in both warp and weft.[120]

Seventeenth-century Italian canvases have been less well studied. It has been pointed out that some of the works Van Dyck painted shortly after his arrival in Italy are on particularly fine canvases and this is the case with the *Portrait of George Gage with Two Attendants* (NG 49) probably painted in Rome in 1622–3 (see pp. 56–9 of this *Bulletin*).[121] Some Italian canvases are very coarse indeed, however. Richard Symonds, writing in 1651–2, quotes a comment by the English painter Robert Walker on the amount of paint used on coarse Italian canvases and their tendency to crack when rolled.[122] Caravaggio's *Saint John the Baptist* (Rome, Musei Capitolini, *c.*1602–3) is painted on a coarse canvas with a thread count of only 8 threads in the vertical direction and 9 in the horizontal, possibly made of hemp rather than linen. Hemp was certainly cultivated in parts of Italy at that time and it has been suggested that Caravaggio used heavy hemp canvases quite frequently.[123] The canvas used by Van Dyck for *The Balbi Children* (NG 6502), painted in Genoa in 1625–7, is almost as coarse (11 threads/cm warp, 8 threads/cm weft) as that described for the Caravaggio picture; a rather similar weight of canvas was used for the *Portrait of Giovanni Battista Cattaneo* (NG 2127), attributed to Van Dyck and thought to have been painted in Genoa at about the same time (9 threads/cm warp, 9–10 threads/cm weft). However, in these cases the fibre used has not been identified. Unfortunately, even on the rare occasions when it is possible to examine the canvas itself,

deterioration of the threads usually makes the identification of the fibres as hemp or linen very difficult. If the coarse outer fibres of flax, or a particularly coarse grade, have been used for the textile, the distinction between flax and hemp is even more difficult.[124]

In order to be primed and used as a painting support, the canvas had to be stretched on a framework, or strainer. Probably this was done by simply lacing the cloth inside the opening of the strainer with cords. The canvas would then be sized and, when dry, primed. The pattern of distortions set up in the fabric from the points of attachment to the framework appear as a regular series of cusps or scallops around the edges of the canvas. The tension pattern is, so to speak, 'fixed' into the textile and may thus be seen in X-radiographs of paintings (Figs. 12 and 13). As it was caused during the first stretching and priming process, it records the original format of the canvas; the presence or absence of this so-called 'primary' cusping may thus provide useful evidence where, for example, it is suspected that the format of a painting has been altered.[125] There is also evidence that canvas might sometimes be primed in larger pieces, such as the long strips cut from the rolls in which the textile would be sold, and then cut to size as required. In the case of the strips, the canvas was attached as described along the length of the piece (the selvedge edges, in fact), but usually only by the corners at the two short sides.[126]

The primed canvas might remain on the same strainer for painting, or it might be restretched, perhaps inside another strainer with cords as before. Sometimes the canvas was stretched against the front surface of a strainer that was only barely larger, being laced into position. It could be nailed to the strainer, wrapping the edges of the canvas around the framework. In these cases, the canvas would in effect be on its final stretcher, ready for framing on completion. As the ground layers would not be thoroughly hardened in such a short time, the second stretching might also produce some distortion around the edge of the canvas ('secondary cusping'), although the original lacing holes would be re-used to some extent.[127] Some illustrations of seventeenth-century artists at work show the canvas stretched within a framework (Fig. 7, p. 16). The poet Sir John Suckling mentions what must, in the context, be a frame of this general type in a letter to his uncle, the Earl of Middlesex, while making a comparative point using Anthony van Dyck at work as an example: '... Van Dike with all his fine Colours and Pensills about him,

25

Fig. 12 Peter Paul Rubens, *Portrait of Thomas Howard, 2nd Earl of Arundel* (NG 2968), 1629–30. Canvas, 67 × 54 cm.

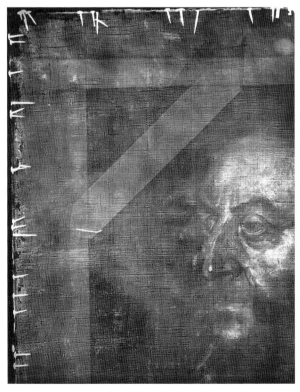

Fig. 13 Peter Paul Rubens, *Portrait of Thomas Howard, 2nd Earl of Arundel*. X-radiograph of top left corner, showing cusping along edge of canvas.

his Frame and right Light, and Everything in order ...'[128] Inventories of artists' property sometimes mention strainers, but they do not necessarily provide evidence of whether the artists primed their own canvases or bought them ready-primed.[129] However, it is clear from the 1673 Rotterdam inventory that ready-primed canvas was available at this date and there are other, earlier, Dutch references to specialist primers.[130] De Mayerne records the method for priming a canvas used by an unnamed Flemish primer – *imprimeur* – and a comment made by a Flemish painter named Portman on how to make good a picture on canvas that has split 'by the fault of the primer'.[131] If canvas primers were working in London in the 1630s, it seems inconceivable that they were not to be found in the very much more developed world of the Antwerp artistic community, particularly as so many painters from this region had come to London to work. However, undoubtedly painters also stretched and primed their own canvases; the inventory of the estate of Johanna Daragon, wife of the painter Johannes Cossiers, mentions a debt of twenty-four guilders for an order of linen for painting. The inventory of Rubens's estate also records a payment to one Hans Diericx for *schilderlynwaet* (painters' linen).[132]

Like the panels, canvases in Antwerp could be bought in standard sizes. The Van Haecht/Wiael inventory includes two primed canvases on strainers, each two *doecken* large. Other canvases and pictures are described as *halffdoecxkens* and *quaertkens doecxkens*. The pattern of double, single, half- and quarter-sizes occurs in other inventories.[133] The dimensions of a *doek* in Antwerp probably related to the Brabant ell measure, or to some commonly used canvas width. As frames were also available in standard sizes, it seems very likely that the standard canvas formats bore some relation to those for panels. By the middle of the century, if not earlier, standard-sized canvases were available in cities in the Northern Netherlands and Rome, the sizes here being indicated by price; by the 1670s (and, again, very probably earlier) they were available in London.[134]

Copper panels

Although neither Rubens nor Van Dyck seem particularly to have favoured the use of metal panels as supports for painting (only four paintings by Rubens on copper are known, for example), copper panels were quite widely used in the seventeenth century, particularly in Italy and in the Netherlands generally. In a letter referring, with great sadness, to the death of his friend the German painter Adam Elsheimer, Rubens commented that Elsheimer's widow should send a painting of *The Flight into Egypt* on a copper panel to Antwerp for sale, as many people there were interested in small works.[135]

It is thought that the development of etching and engraving during the sixteenth century may have contributed to the use of copper plates as supports for painting, particularly as many painters also produced intaglio prints. The Antwerp painter David Teniers the Younger, for example, who painted landscapes and genre scenes, also produced etchings; a series of four paintings of activities representing the seasons in the National Gallery Collection (*Spring*, *Summer*, *Autumn* and *Winter*, NG 857–60, dated about 1644) are on copper plates. These are quite small, ranging from 21.9 × 16 cm (*Summer*) to 22.1 × 16.5 cm (*Spring*). *Pan pursuing Syrinx* (Plate 3, p. 8), in which the figures were painted by Van Dyck's first master Hendrick van Balen the Elder and the landscape by a follower of Jan Brueghel the Elder, perhaps shortly after 1615, is only slightly larger at 25 × 19.4 cm. Many paintings on copper supports (and, indeed, many etchings) are larger than this. The use of plates previously used for etching or engraving seems to be fairly uncommon, however.[136] Copper plates were occasionally coated with another metal (tin or zinc). In order that the paint should adhere to the smooth metal surface, it was necessary to prepare the plate before use. Recommended treatments included abrasion, and rubbing the plate with garlic, which is sticky when first applied; the garlic acts as a wetting agent, preventing surface tension effects between smooth shiny metal and oil paint interfering with the application of paint and formation of the film. Another treatment was to wipe the plate over with linseed oil. A thin oil-based ground, usually containing lead white mixed with other pigments, was then generally applied.

The Preparatory Layers

Panels were prepared with a white ground of chalk (calcium carbonate) in a medium of animal glue; in Antwerp, this was normally done by the panel-maker. The panel was then scraped down with a knife until it was even and the process could be repeated. It should be noted that both Henry Peacham and the author of MS Harley 6376 refer to this stage as 'whiting' the panel; priming was the next stage, where one or sometimes two layers of a suitable pigment mixture in linseed oil were applied. De Mayerne's informants preferred a mixture of lead white and

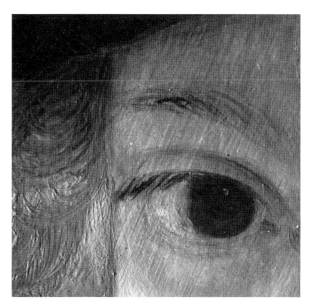

Fig. 14 Peter Paul Rubens, *Portrait of Susanna Lunden (?)*. Detail photographed at ×4. The priming is clearly visible through the thin paint on the sitter's forehead. A point, perhaps the brush handle, was used to draw curls of hair in the wet paint.

umber; the author of MS Harley 6376 suggested lead white with a little red lead in the first layer, with the addition of the brown earth pigment Spanish brown and umber in the second. He noted that the first layer should be thinned with oil as some oil would inevitably sink into the white layer below; if this was not done the colours applied above would tend to sink. This layer acted as an isolation layer, as well as providing a fairly neutral brownish or greyish tint to the ground, the density of which would depend on the thickness of the layer.[137]

In those panels by Rubens and Van Dyck in the National Gallery Collection that have been examined, the priming layer is often extremely thin. It is thus difficult to identify the medium present, but in Rubens's *Samson and Delilah* (NG 6461) and in the greyish priming in Van Dyck's *Charity* it is oil.[138] It is perfectly possible that a thin priming or isolation layer, in some neutral tint, in oil medium, was applied by the panel-maker or the *witter*, perhaps routinely. If the artist wanted a particular type of priming (or none at all) he could ask for it, or apply it himself in the studio. The streaky appearance of Rubens's brown, ochre and lead white-containing primings (characteristic, perhaps, of the use of a broad, comparatively stiff, bristle brush) has often been noted: it can clearly be seen in *Samson and Delilah* and the *Portrait of Susanna Lunden* (NG 852), for example (Fig. 14). Its application is more obvious in the oil sketches, none more so than *A Lion Hunt* (NG 853.1), where its application is particularly random.[139] Rubens's primings are so characteristic that it might be supposed that they must have been applied in his studio, but streaky primings may be found on other contemporary panels.[140]

Canvas grounds are rather variable in their colour and pigment content, and in the number of layers present, depending on local practice and, partly, on materials available. The method of application seems to be fairly constant: the chosen pigments were ground in linseed oil and spread thinly and evenly across the canvas with a knife, working in well. This would require particular care with a closely woven, calendered fabric like ticking; equally, it can be seen that the interstices in a coarse, open-weave canvas would take up quite a lot of paint. After the paint had dried, the surface was scraped with a knife, cutting away knots and protrusions from the fabric, and polished with a pumice stone. Another layer might then be applied.[141] The author of MS Harley 6376 points out that the colour should be as thick as that used for painting, and that the pigments used in the lower ground layer could be quite coarsely ground; Richard Symonds, recording the practice of the painter Giovanni Angelo Canini in Rome, observed similarly that they should be finer in the upper ground layer. This is generally borne out in practice. In MS Harley 6376 a mixture comprising lead white, red lead and the earth pigments Spanish brown and umber is suggested, with the addition of a little black in the upper layer if required. This would dry well, but the author warns against the use of too much red lead as the mixture would 'pill of in a length of time but especially on cloth when you roul it up'. De Mayerne's informants suggested English brown-red (an ochre), burnt ochre, lead white with a little umber, yellow ochre, lead white with a little red ochre and umber, and bole (a clay deriving its colour from the red iron oxide it contains) with umber.[142] The mixture used by Canini included red earth, a little lead white, *creta* and a little black; the ordinary canvas primers seem to have omitted the lead white which would act as a drier as well as modifying the colour slightly. The word '*creta*', chalk, could apparently signify other white silicaceous earths and clays. Symonds also noted that the earth used for making bricks could be ground and used for priming.[143]

Analysis of the materials present in the grounds of the paintings by Van Dyck in the National Gallery Collection shows that there is a close relationship between the chemical composition of the ground of a painting Van Dyck produced in Rome and that of the grounds of other paintings produced in Rome at that time – those of Poussin, for example – although visually the grounds may look rather different when observed under the microscope. The grounds of paintings produced in London or Brussels are dissimilar both to those produced in Rome and to each other (this is discussed further in the article on Van Dyck's paintings, pp. 50–83). This suggests that painters had their canvases primed locally, or bought them ready primed; as with the panels, another ground layer could be applied in the studio if desired. Symonds's comment on the use of an earth used for brick-making is interesting as the composition of the Roman and Genoese grounds (or the lowest layer in the case of those paintings, like the portrait of *George Gage*, where there are two) is reminiscent of locally quarried earths rather than a specifically chosen pigment mixture. Seventeenth-century Roman grounds are often reddish or brownish in colour and often single-layered, but may be translucent and the actual iron oxide content may be rather low. However, Symonds's mention of the addition of some form of white earth suggests that this practice cannot be ruled out.

The grounds applied in London often appear to have a two-layered structure, of which the lower one is reddish or orangish brown and sometimes markedly translucent; the upper is grey and may have been applied to order, or in the studio. Often chalk is present in the lower red-brown layer, mixed with ochre pigments. This is seen in Van Dyck's *Equestrian Portrait of Charles I* and *Lady Elizabeth Thimbelby and Dorothy, Viscountess Andover*. The grounds of Rubens's rather earlier *Portrait of Thomas Howard, 2nd Earl of Arundel* (NG 2968, painted during his visit to London in 1629–30 (Fig. 12, p. 26), and the central part of his *Minerva protects Pax from Mars* ('*Peace and War*') (NG 46, discussed on pp. 89–95) of about the same date, are very similar in translucency and appearance. However, other translucent white earths were also used, such as china clay (kaolin). A white clay of this type was found in the ground of Van Dyck's 'Great Peece', and the use of pipeclay in the ground of this painting was thought to be responsible for the poor adhesion between the paint and the support as early as 1676.[144]

A probable reason for the use of a locally quarried earth, or the additions of materials like chalk or china clay (which are, for practical purposes, colourless in oil medium), was their cheapness and ready availability. The main function of this lowest layer, after all, was to help counteract the absorbency of the textile support and to provide an even working surface. Other pigments present, such as lead white, red lead or earth pigments, would improve the drying of the oil and add colour if desired. Other factors need to be borne in mind, however: these include the working properties of the mixture and the need to avoid absorption of the oil medium from the paint layers above, which causes them to 'sink', that is, to dry with a matt surface. Some pigments, notably umbers, were particularly likely to cause this, although they were suggested for use in grounds as they dry well.

The Practice and Materials of Painting
Preliminary drawings and *modelli*

The finished painting marked the last stage in the evolution of the composition. It was preceded by preliminary drawings and sketches in which the design of the composition was developed to the point where it could be transferred to the final panel or canvas, being drawn initially perhaps with black chalk or charcoal, then reworked with a brush and fluid paint (see pp. 50–83).[145] This might be backed up by drawings from a model for particular figures or poses where required, or even from a collection of patterns for particular features; Van Dyck, for example, used such drawings for the hands of his sitters, according to Everhard Jabach's account to de Piles, and also for plant and landscape forms.[146] It is possible to see such a progression taking place in the series of drawings for one of Van Dyck's earliest works, *The Carrying of the Cross*, probably painted during 1617 and 1618 for the Dominican church of Saint Paul's, Antwerp, one of a series of works commissioned from the leading painters in Antwerp, including Rubens, Jacob Jordaens, and Van Dyck's first master, Hendrick van Balen, an august company for the young Van Dyck. The final drawing in the series, which is in black chalk overlaid by a more precise drawing in pen, ink and washes, is squared up for the final transfer to the panel.[147]

A final, small-scale *modello* of the composition might be made in oil, in grisaille or in colour, to a greater or lesser degree of finish. This could be shown to the patron commissioning the work for his approval; it could also be used as a guide when the final painting was produced. A great many such *modelli* by Rubens survive; examples in the National Gallery Collection include *Saint Bavo about to receive*

Plate 8 Peter Paul Rubens, *Minerva and Mercury conduct the Duke of Buckingham to the Temple of Virtue* (NG 187). Oak, 64 × 63.7 cm.

the Monastic Habit at Ghent (NG 57), painted for a triptych intended for the high altar of Saint Bavo, Ghent, which was commissioned in 1611 or 1612, and *Minerva and Mercury conduct the Duke of Buckingham to the Temple of Virtue* (Plate 8). This is the preparatory sketch for a ceiling painting in the London house of the Duke, commissioned around 1625. The production of *modelli* as a regular part of the compositional process, as it appears to be in the work of Rubens, must relate to the part played by his studio in the production of the final works themselves.[148] Although Van Dyck also produced small-scale versions of compositions in oil, he did not make as much use of *modelli* as Rubens, preferring to use drawings instead; his assistants worked from a sketch for portraits, according to Jabach's account. Little is known about the workings of Van Dyck's studio at any stage, but during his years travelling through Italy he cannot have had much studio assistance. In Genoa he would perhaps have been able to draw on the community of Flemish painters there; he was friendly with Cornelis de Wael and is known to have had the occasional collaboration of Jan Roos. During his time in Genoa, he may have made small oil sketches of the heads of some of his sitters, particularly women. The sketch could be made in the sitter's house and the final portrait on canvas could then be worked up in the studio, which it might have been deemed inappropriate for the sitter to visit. A study on canvas (in the National Museum of

American Art, Washington) was made for the portrait of *Elena Grimaldi Cattaneo* (in the National Gallery of Art, Washington); the red flower worn by the sitter in the study is replaced by a red parasol in the painting.[149]

Painting materials: pigments

The painting materials generally available for use in the seventeenth century included the natural mineral blue pigments, ultramarine and azurite; the yellow, red and brown earth pigments; the manufactured pigments, such as vermilion (which also occurred naturally), lead white, red lead, lead-tin yellow, smalt and verdigris; the red and yellow lake pigments; the insoluble blue plant dyestuff, indigo; and, finally, the different blacks. There was also a greatly increased use of artificially prepared blue and green copper pigments. The differences observed between the paint of a mid-to-late sixteenth-century painter and one working fifty or sixty years later lie more in the way the materials are used, not in the materials themselves. In practice, there were some changes, partly because certain pigments, such as azurite, became very scarce; partly, perhaps, for aesthetic reasons. Scarcity and expense were certainly factors in the changing pattern of use seen in the blue pigments, which are discussed below. However, a pigment like verdigris (the collective name for the blue-green basic copper acetates), which was 'nothing else but the rust of brasse ... as you may see many times upon foule candlesticks' and was manufactured from copper plates and vinegar, or acidic wine residues, was neither scarce nor particularly expensive, although its quality was variable and so-called distilled verdigris (neutral copper acetate, recrystallised from vinegar) was said to be preferable.[150] Its use, however, tended to decrease in the seventeenth century, particularly in landscape painting. It is possible that, for naturalistic landscapes, the colour was not to the taste of the times; more subtle, less strident foliage greens could be obtained by other means. It was more successfully used in the painting of drapery or clothing and was employed by Van Dyck, for example, for the green clothes of the central boy in *The Balbi Children* (NG 6502), painted in Genoa in about 1625–7 (see p. 63). Like other copper-containing pigments, verdigris was also a useful drier for blacks and other poorly drying pigments and it continued to be recommended for this purpose.[151]

Apart from the earths, most of the widely used pigments were manufactured. Verdigris, lead white and red lead had been manufactured from early times; the synthesis of vermilon was also a well-established process. Some were by-products of other industries: lead-tin yellow, known as *massicot* or *masticot*, derived originally from the ceramics industry; green and blue verditers were made from the copper nitrate solution remaining from the refining of silver; some red lakes, such as those from cochineal, were made from dyestuff extracted from dyed textile waste. The conditions of manufacture could thus be controlled to get a desired grade or colour of product. Many seventeenth-century sources indicate that lead-tin yellow 'type I', the form used in Northern Europe – and generally throughout Europe in the seventeenth century – was available in pale and dark shades.[152] Very few recipes for the preparation of the pigment, as such, are known; its source probably lay in another old and well-understood technology, the preparation of colorants for ceramic glazes.[153]

The chemistry of the process by which the verditers (Plate 9) were produced could not have been understood at that date. Although recipes for the preparation of artificial copper-containing blue pigments exist from early times, it is clear, from the seemingly random inclusion of unnecessary ingredients in early recipes, which were discarded as time went on, that comprehension of the craft involved and the conditions to be used was acquired gradually through practice. The products were also variable.[154] In fifteenth- and sixteenth-century versions of these recipes, the ingredients were usually verdigris, lime, sal ammoniac (ammonium chloride) and vinegar or water. It seems likely, however, that these methods for making blues were not in current use.[155] De Mayerne, inquisitive experimental scientist, was intrigued by the way in which blue verditer was produced and must have recognised there was some connection between this and the old traditional 'azures'. Even though his interest may have been partly antiquarian, de Mayerne copied out several

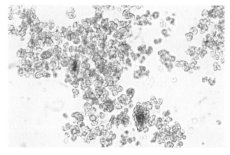

Plate 9 Blue verditer, synthetic basic copper carbonate, prepared by Peter Mactaggart. Photographed at a magnification of 700×; actual magnification 420×.

such recipes from earlier Italian and English sources. He mentions that he had been told that the green liquor from silver refining was used to make the verditers; having observed the blue colour obtained when quick lime and sal ammoniac were dissolved in water in a copper basin, he speculated that the addition of sal ammoniac and chalk or lead white to the silver refiners' liquor might indeed give something like blue verditer. He was also told that a method had been discovered accidentally by someone who had poured aqua regia (one part of concentrated nitric acid to three parts of concentrated hydrochloric acid) onto lead white or chalk. In a marginal note he added that this did not work when he tried it, not surprisingly as no copper was present.[156] However, it is likely that this method was, in fact, used: it is described, with one important difference, later in the century by Christopher Merrett, the translator of Antonio Neri's influential work on glass-making, *L'arte vetraria* (Florence 1612); the recipe for common blue ashes (blue verditer), *slechte blaù assen*, in the Antwerp sketchbook, mentioned above, is very similar. The difference was that, in the first case, copper plates were present and, in the second, copper filings were dissolved in the nitric acid used.[157] In the case of the production of blue verditer, unlike lead-tin yellow, neither craft nor technology appear to have been well understood; it was not at all clear to the early seventeenth-century English manufacturers why the product was only sometimes blue and, more often, the less valuable green: Merrett was one author who commented on the unpredictability of the process. The curious suggestion in the Antwerp sketchbook recipe that the product should be washed with smalt to obtain the blue ashes indicates that here, too, the product was liable to be green. More recent research has shown that the colour of the product depends on the temperature at which the reaction is carried out and how much the solution is stirred, factors that the seventeenth-century maker would only appreciate over time, by trial and error.[158]

The manufacture of pigments

The manufacturing, preparation and distribution of pigments in the early part of the seventeenth century seem to have been particularly well developed in the Northern Netherlands.[159] Initially manufacturers tended to specialise in a particular pigment: vermilion, say, or smalt, or lead white; later they might broaden their field of interest. As well as making the pigment the producer also prepared it to some degree by washing, grinding and whatever else was necessary; certainly they could be obtained ready ground at retail outlets.[160] This also applied to the preparation of natural mineral pigments. The letters patent granted to an ochre refiner in the Forest of Dean, Gloucestershire, in 1626 mention mills, vessels for washing and drying rooms for the grinding and refining of red ochre and the brown burnt ochre, Spanish brown.[161] As a result, the pigment would have reached the retailer in such a form that it would not require very much more preparation by the artist, assuming that it had not been adulterated. Richard Symonds was informed by Mrs Boardman, a portrait painter and copyist, in 1650–1 that vermilion was adulterated with red ochre; very possibly this was done earlier also.[162] The Dutch pigments, notably vermilion and smalt, had a good reputation; to this was added quite aggressive marketing, as the problems encountered by William Twynyho, Abraham Baker and John Artogh, who were awarded a patent for making smalt in London in 1605, seem to indicate.[163]

Painting materials: the oil medium

It is not known how much treatment the oil used by painters would have received by the time it reached the retailer and how much the artist would carry out himself, or have done on his behalf. Leaving oil on a window sill to decolorise is very easy: something the artist might do as a matter of routine. Removing cloudy traces of mucilaginous matter or other contaminants would be rather more troublesome, although not difficult. An important concern of many of de Mayerne's informants, including Paul van Somer, Daniel Mytens and Anthony van Dyck, was the clarity and paleness of the oil they used. De Mayerne was given many accounts of how oil should be purified, bleached and its drying properties improved by heating it with litharge (lead monoxide) or minium (red lead, lead tetroxide), or another suitable drier. The commonest method of purification consisted of mixing the oil with rainwater in which salt and/ or alum had been dissolved; this would help to coagulate mucilaginous plant material which would settle out. The mixture was stirred, allowed to stand, for some days as a rule, and the oil was separated off. The process could be repeated; the oil was then washed to remove the salts. Before this the oil might be filtered through sand, as described by van Somer.[164] Bleaching the fugitive plant colorants which gave the virgin oil its yellow colour could be done by leaving it in the sun, but, as both van Somer and Mytens pointed out, this also caused the oil to thicken; if this was not wanted, they suggested that March was a good month for carrying out the process as the sun was not strong enough for the polymerisation of the oil to be encouraged.[165]

In his heading for instructions for thickening oil by leaving it to stand over hot ashes, a method with which Mytens's name was associated, de Mayerne in effect summarised the properties of a heat-prepolymerised oil: it was thicker; it had improved drying properties; it prevented pigments from sinking to the bottom of the paint layer.[166] The paint would be less likely to shrink, and thus to wrinkle, as it dried. The slightly raised refractive index of the oil also slightly increases the depth or saturation of the colour and gives a smooth, even, glossy finish, without brush marks. The method of heating the oil in this recipe is unusually gentle and, as oil does not conduct heat particularly efficiently, any prepolymerisation – the linking together of the triglyceride molecules present by carbon–oxygen or carbon–carbon bonds – would only be partial. Most methods for heat-bodied oils required them to be heated carefully over lead salts, with stirring as a rule, for a fairly brief period: van Somer's instructions were that the oil should be heated over litharge until it began to boil (that is, evolved bubbles of steam, from absorbed moisture, and carbon dioxide); it was then removed from the fire until the ebullition ceased and then replaced, this process being repeated five or six times.[167] As the mixture was stirred, probably oxygen would be incorporated, depending on how briskly this was done; thus at least a proportion of the bonds formed during the thickening process would be carbon–oxygen, carbon–carbon bonds being formed under conditions where oxygen was excluded.[168] It is unlikely that such a process would be carried out on a very large scale: little more than a litre or so of oil was heated at a time, according to most seventeenth-century sources, so it would not be impossible for the artist to carry it out himself. It could have been carried out on behalf of the retailer for sale, as oils, treated and untreated, were used in other related trades, such as varnish-making.

In his conversations with de Mayerne, Van Dyck expressed a preference for linseed oil, which he described as the best of all.[169] He was certainly not unusual in this; Rubens too employed linseed oil to a great extent, although only walnut oil was detected in the *Elevation of the Cross* in Antwerp cathedral.[170] Because walnut oil yellowed less initially during drying, it was traditionally recommended for use with pigments whose colour was particularly affected by yellowing of the medium, such as whites and blues; in practice it is quite often found in light-coloured paint in general, including flesh-colour and pale yellow. On balance, apart from the *Portrait of George Gage with Two Attendants* (NG 49) where walnut oil was used for black paint as well as for cream-coloured paint in the sky, this practice has been followed and walnut oil has been found in whites and blues, although not consistently. It was used for Charity's blue shawl, for example, but in *The Abbé Scaglia adoring the Virgin and Child* (NG 4889) linseed oil was used for the Virgin's robe, although walnut oil was used in the sky. Sometimes the oils were heat bodied, or, apparently, partially so, as in the case of much of the paint in *The Abbé Scaglia adoring the Virgin and Child*. In the case of the dark blue paint of the Virgin's robe, which contains the poorly drying pigments ultramarine and indigo, this was perhaps to aid drying, but the artist may have had the additional aim of obtaining a smooth, glossy surface, without notable brush marks and a wrinkle-free paint. In the case of a partial heat-prepolymerisation, it is not possible to say if the paint was particularly gently heated, so genuinely only partially prepolymerised, or if heat-bodied oil was added to paint which had been ground in ordinary oil.

Van Dyck consistently incorporated a trace of pine resin in the medium used in areas of translucent paint like the pinkish-red glaze on the Virgin's robe in *The Abbé Scaglia adoring the Virgin and Child* and the dark red glaze on the curtain in *Portrait of a Woman and Child* (NG 3011). This addition results in a more transparent, glossier paint, very much more effective as a glaze or as a deep translucent shadow, as the refractive index of the paint is slightly raised so that it is closer to that of the pigments present.[171] Probably it was added in the form of a small amount of ordinary pine resin varnish. This, too, was a traditional practice in Netherlandish painting. Rubens included a little pine resin in green glaze-like paint in *An Autumn Landscape with a View of Het Steen in the Early Morning* and in the dark brown shadowy background paint of *The Brazen Serpent*. Pine resin was also detected in some of the paint in the *Elevation of the Cross* and in a red glazed shadow on the drapery of a figure in the *Drunken Silenus supported by Satyrs* (NG 853).

Interestingly, a trace of larch resin, that is, Venice turpentine, was detected in red lake-containing paint present on the strip of re-used canvas attached to the right of the main piece used for the *Portrait of George Gage with Two Attendants*; the red paint was not part of the composition and was painted over (see pp. 57–8 and p. 87, note 7). This picture was painted in Rome. Recipes for Venice turpentine varnishes occur in Italian sources and it has been identified in a varnish on the *Portrait of a Lady with the Attributes of Saint Agatha* (NG 24), attributed to Sebastiano del Piombo and probably painted in Rome around 1540; it is not known when the varnish was applied, but it must date from before the early eighteenth century.[172] Its use in this way has not previously been observed (although it should be said that it is extremely difficult to detect); conceivably it was present in the red lake paint because a little varnish was usually added and it happened to be a Venice turpentine varnish. The conventional pine resin was present in a similar red glaze in *The Balbi Children*. Some knowledge of Venice turpentine had certainly found its way into Rubens's studio, however, as it is mentioned in the Antwerp sketchbook: it was thought less suitable for a very good varnish than Strasbourg turpentine (fir balsam).[173] Paul van Somer and Van Dyck also discussed Venice turpentine varnish with de Mayerne: from the record of the conversation with Van Dyck, it could even be assumed that 'ordinary painters' varnish' was prepared from Venice turpentine.[174] As a physician, de Mayerne would have been very familar with Venice turpentine, which was an ingredient in various medical preparations and could be distilled to give a volatile oil and a solid product in exactly the same manner as ordinary pine resin.[175] However, it was not used for 'ordinary painters' varnish', in London at least: apart from the fact that pine resin made as good, or better, a varnish for most ordinary purposes, if a little darker, the import duty imposed on it suggests that Venice turpentine was far too expensive for widespread use. If Van Dyck used it while he was in London (and there is evidence that he bought mastic, but no record of Venice turpentine, although he was said to have used a Venice turpentine retouching varnish) it has not been confirmed so far.[176]

Artists' suppliers, apothecaries and colourmen

Early seventeenth-century artists probably bought their materials at an apothecary's shop, the traditional suppliers of pigments because most pigments – and many other artists' materials – were still categorised as drugs. The 1642 *Rates of Merchandizes* still listed the duties to be paid on vermilion, *flory* (woad indigo), *generall* (a pigment of lead-tin yellow type), gum lac (the source of lac dyestuff), lapis lazuli (the

mineral source of ultramarine), oil of turpentine, orpiment, red and white lead, Venice and common turpentine, verdigris, 'varnish' and umber under *Drugges*. Indigo, ochre, linseed oil, rosin, smalt and verditer, for example, were listed separately.[177] The London apothecaries, like many of their European counterparts, had arisen from the same roots as the grocers and the spicers. They formed an autonomous section of the Grocers Company until they received their own charter in 1618, and probably concentrated rather more on medicinal materials, including pigments, but it is perfectly possible that someone who called himself a grocer sold pigments as well. In the latter part of the seventeenth century the position was complicated by the existence of two other related groups: the druggists, originally probably wholesalers who remained under the Grocers Company when the apothecaries left, and the dispensing chemists, who fulfilled a rather similar role to the apothecaries. The boundaries between these trades were not very distinct and clearly druggists might have included pigments among the goods they sold to retailers.[178]

These may not have been the only source of artists' materials: several sixteenth-century Serjeant Painters are known to have supplied materials for certain projects and one, Andrew Wright, who died in 1543, was a manufacturer of yellow lake pigment.[179] Other sixteenth-century Painter-Stainers also supplied materials, but it is not known if this was purely for particular court commissions or as a business venture. It is possible that some seventeenth-century members of the Company did the same. De Mayerne mentions several places where pigments could be obtained in London, all within the City walls and quite near the Exchange, including the oddly named 'Pabstset allée', by which he may have meant Popes Head Alley.[180] These are all very near present-day Cheapside and Bucklersbury, the area where spicers and apothecaries had plied their trades for centuries, as described by John Stow: 'This whole streete, called Bucklesburie, on both the sides throughout, is possessed of Grocers and Apothecaries.'[181] However, many artists lived outside the City, as de Mayerne did himself, in St Martin's Lane.[182] There were suppliers in the Holborn area by 1651–2, when Richard Symonds referred to one Fenn the Liegois – like many of his potential customers, he was of Netherlandish stock – who lived in Purpoole Lane (the area of the modern Grays Inn Road) and demanded five shillings for a pot of colours the size of a walnut.[183]

In Antwerp the apothecaries came under the *Meerseniers* (Mercers) guild. Here, too, the trade of

Fig. 15 Jerome Franken the Younger, *Jan Snellinck's Shop*, 1621. Panel, 94 × 124.7 cm. Brussels, Koninklijk Museum voor Oude Kunst (no. 2628).

kruidenier, spice merchant or grocer, developed during the sixteenth and early seventeenth centuries in a number of ways, not only in Antwerp itself; many merchants emigrated during the 1580s and were able to flourish and expand their businesses in their new homes, notably in the United Provinces.[184] In the Northern Netherlands in the sixteenth century there was no clear distinction between the trades of grocer and apothecary, much as in England, and a similar situation probably obtained in Antwerp at this time. Throughout the registers of the Guild of Saint Luke, names are assigned to trades related to painting in the broad sense, such as picture dealer, brush-maker (rarely) and even varnish-maker – one Heynderick van Thienen is described as such in 1585–6 – but also to other trades, including that of *kruidenier* (grocer).[185] Probably most of these sold pigments among their other merchandise. However they developed, there were people described as colour merchants in Antwerp by the 1580s. Four colour merchants are listed in the Guild records for 1585–6: Merten Alewyn, Pieter van Eycken, Davidt Meermans and Andries Coeck, three of whom reappear in those for 1588–9 (Alewyn, Coeck and van Eycken), together with Cornelis Nuyts.[186]

The inventory of the estate of Maria van Flinckenborch and her husband the colour merchant Aernoult Hoegaerts the Elder, made in March 1609, records the sale and the receipt of money for large quantities of certain pigments, mainly blue and green, including two grades of ashes, two grades of smalt, coarse *stroyblauw* and *olie smalt* (oil smalt), and *asur gruen* (possibly malachite). The only other pigment recorded is a red lake pigment at 10 and 12 stuivers

the ounce. Perhaps Hoegaerts traded in the cheaper pigments as well, but they were not recorded in the final estate.[187] It appears that, in the inventories of artists' estates, only the valuable pigments – the different grades of ashes and smalt, occasionally ultramarine and good quality lake pigments – are recorded.

The names of several colour merchants appear in artists' inventories in the first decades of the seventeenth century. The estate of Aernoult Hoegaerts received payment for 24³/₄ pounds of fine ashes at 9 guilders the pound, bought in 1608 by another colour merchant, Jeremias Cock. A Jeremias Cocq, described as a merchant, is mentioned in a letter by Rubens to Hans Oberholtzer discussing arrangements for the transport of some paintings in 1620: presumably this is the same man.[188] While it is not clear from this if Cocq ever acted as a picture dealer as well, there are occasional references to art dealers in the Northern Netherlands also trading in pigments at this time, and certainly later on in the 1640s.[189] The situation in Antwerp appears to have been similar: some artists were also picture dealers – as were some panel-makers, Hans van Haecht, for example – and some dealers were also colour merchants. They may also have maintained their painting trade. David Remeus or Remeeus apparently had a profitable shop selling gilded frames, pictures and pigments, but is recorded in the *Liggeren* of the guild as a painter from the time he became a master, in 1581, until he registered his twenty-first and last pupil in 1622–3. He is also described as a colour merchant, to whom money was owed, in the 1620 inventory of the estate of the painter Peter de Noville the Elder.[190] The inventory of his estate, made in August 1626, records a quantity of gold leaf and the value of the shop wares handed over to Remeus's widow, Joanna de Prince: 2939 guilders 2 stuivers. Outstanding accounts with various customers, including Hendrick van Balen and Lucas 'living at the painter Rubens's [establishment]' are also listed. Joanna de Prince continued the business in pigments and in 1630 married the painter Jacob or Jacques Spaegnaert (Spaeingaert, etc.), who was clearly successful as a colour merchant during the 1630s, but seems not to have registered any pupils as a painter.[191]

Jan Snellinck the Elder is also described as a painter in the inventory of his, and his wife's, estate, taken in 1638, but he, too, was a picture dealer from the 1580s onwards (Fig. 15). The estate was also owed money for pigments, principally green and blue ashes.[192] It is not surprising that the widows of painters sometimes sold off the more valuable pigments; a payment of 36 guilders is recorded from Rubens's estate to the widow of Hans van Milder for green ashes.[193]

The trade in pigments, both naturally occurring and manufactured, was considerable. In England, for example, the 1642 *Rates of Merchandizes* lists duties payable on the import of almost all the pigments then used, including ochre. As England exported red and yellow ochres, presumably this was a different colour or grade.[194] As a result, the availability of pigments did not differ greatly between one centre and another. One example of a locally available pigment which appears, from current evidence at least, to be particularly associated with Italy, and specifically Rome, is a type of *giallolino* (that is, a pigment of the lead-tin yellow variety), in this case a lead-tin-antimony oxide. Like Naples yellow, lead-tin-antimony oxide probably had its origins in the ceramics industry: antimony, in the form of the oxide, was an ingredient used in the warm yellows decorating the opaque, white, tin-containing glazes on maiolica. It has been found in works dating from the 1620s and earlier so could have been available to the young Van Dyck during his stay in Rome.[195] Richard Symonds commented that there were three or four sorts of *giallolino* on sale in Rome when he was there in 1649–51, some redder, some yellower.[196]

Symonds also noted that there were two or three sorts of green earth available, but the pigment seems to have been little known in London at this time. De Mayerne describes a green bole of little body from Italy that was useful for landscape and could be used in oil; its colour was a dirty green.[197] One variety of green earth that Symonds probably had in mind was a strongly coloured bluish-green celadonite, obtained from near Verona, which had a good reputation because of its superior colour.[198] A strongly coloured green earth is found in Roman landscape paintings of the mid-seventeenth century, for example, those by Claude and Salvator Rosa, but it seems only to have reached Northern Europe much later.

Blue pigments

The blue pigments ultramarine and azurite had always been the most expensive, and contracts and guild statutes had sometimes specified their use, or had forbidden the use of cheaper substitutes. By the seventeenth century, the expense of ultramarine and the scarcity of the basic copper carbonate mineral azurite (principally after the middle of the century)

were factors contributing towards the greatly increased use of smalt and indigo. The fact that smalt and the manufactured green and blue ashes are itemised in Antwerp inventories of artists' property reveals very clearly the value that was placed on them, to say nothing of ultramarine. The inventory of the property of Margriet Briers, the widow of Hendrik van Balen the Elder, includes smalt and several small boxes of ultramarine, in at least two grades; the only other pigment listed is a red, Florentine lake.[199]

The laborious process by which ultramarine was separated from calcite and pyrites impurities also present in lapis lazuli resulted in several grades of the pigment. The best grade, with the largest particles and fewest impurities, separated out first; the last, containing much colourless material and rather few, small blue particles, was often known as ultramarine ash.[200] Where its use was required, ultramarine was frequently paid for by the client commissioning the work; this may sometimes have been the case for azurite also, although it is mentioned infrequently. In 1626, 45 guilders was paid for an ounce of ultramarine for Rubens's *Assumption of the Virgin*, painted for Antwerp Cathedral.[201] Charles I was reported to have given ultramarine to the value of £500 to be shared between Van Dyck and the painter Mrs Anne Carlisle.[202] In 1642, Jacob Jordaens received nine guilders for an unspecified amount of *assur blaeu* used in a painting of *The Visitation*, commissioned for the church in Rupelmonde, near Antwerp, in 1641; from the cost and description this was perhaps azurite rather than ultramarine.[203] The position was no different in Italy: on 7 June 1632, the Bolognese painter Guercino recorded the receipt of payment for the purchase of ultramarine and the canvas for two paintings executed for Reggio Cathedral.[204] Ultramarine was often used over an underpaint containing another blue, or even mixed with another blue. Rubens used ultramarine with smalt and lead white for the sky in *Minerva protects Pax from Mars* ('*Peace and War*'). Van Dyck used an underpaint of smalt and white under a thin ultramarine glaze in the sky of the *Equestrian Portrait of Charles I*; indigo was used in the underpaint for the blue robes in *Charity* and *The Abbé Scaglia adoring the Virgin and Child* (see pp. 65–6, 71–3). In these paintings the ultramarine was of reasonable quality, with quite large particles and little impurity.

The use of azurite declined markedly as time went on. Van Dyck used the pigment for Lord Bernard Stuart's clothing in *Lord John Stuart and his Brother, Lord Bernard Stuart*, but scumbled over an

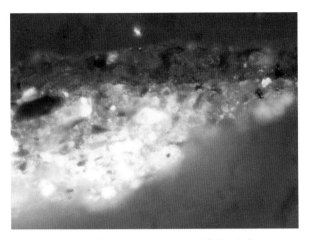

Plate 10 Peter Paul Rubens, *Peasants with Cattle by a Stream in a Woody Landscape ('The Watering Place')* (NG 4815), *c*.1620. Cross-section through dark green foliage paint. The uppermost layer comprises azurite and a yellow lake pigment; the layer below contains in addition lead white and lead-tin yellow. The lowest layer present, the pale blue sky paint, consists of lead white and ultramarine. Photographed at a magnification of 400×; actual magnification 350×.

undermodelling of indigo mixed with lead white (see pp. 80–1). Azurite is a greener blue than ultramarine and was often used as a constituent of greens, mixed with lead-tin yellow 'type I' or a yellow lake pigment. It occurs mixed with yellow lake, ochre or lead-tin yellow in the landscape and foliage greens of Rubens's *Peasants with Cattle by a Stream in a Woody Landscape ('The Watering Place')* (NG 4815, *c*.1615–22, Plate 10), and was used for the more intense greens in Van Dyck's *Equestrian Portrait of Charles I*. Rubens used azurite mixed with lead white in the sky of his early version of *The Judgement of Paris* (NG 6379), thought to have been painted shortly before he left for Italy in 1600, and similarly in his *Portrait of Susanna Lunden* (NG 852), of about 1622–5, but on other occasions – in the sky of '*The Watering Place*', for example – he used ultramarine mixed with lead white. A blue-green verditer might substitute for the more expensive azurite in sketches, such as *Saint Bavo about to receive the Monastic Habit at Ghent*, where it is used for the cloak of the mounted figure in the right-hand wing, and in the skirt of a female saint on the left. Although Rubens used azurite widely in greens, he also used mixtures with a blue-green verditer, in, for example, his later version of *The Judgement of Paris* (NG 194), painted around 1632–5.

Both Rubens and Van Dyck made extensive use of the blue-green verditers, smalt and indigo, and clearly these were by far the most widely used blues.

It is evident both from inventories of artists' property and from the examination of samples from paintings that both smalt and verditer were available in different shades and degrees of coarseness. The estate of the colour merchant Aernoult Hoegaerts received two payments for the pigments from the painter Joos de Momper during 1607; the first was for four and a quarter pounds of blue *olie smalt* at two guilders the pound, and the second was for a bag of fine ashes weighing three pounds, four and three-quarter ounces at eight guilders the pound.[205] It is difficult to judge the relative prices of the two pigments from this evidence alone, but it appears that, on average, smalt was the cheaper of the two. This is confirmed by the London prices de Mayerne noted and to some extent by those in another price list in MS Sloane 1990, the notebook in which much of de Mayerne's work was first written down, often by his collaborators.[206] In the first list, ashes were priced at one shilling (12 pence) to six shillings an ounce; the units are missing from the smalt prices, but it was sold by the pound, like lead white and the earth pigment brown red, and was thus relatively cheap.[207] The source of the second list, which is written in French (rather than a mixture of French and English) is unknown; the prices are all by the pound and, on the whole, are more expensive than the first list. Curiously, smalt is not listed (or not under an unequivocal name), but, while the cheapest of the three grades of ashes cost £1 a pound, little more than lead white, the most expensive was £6 a pound, the most expensive pigment listed. The next most expensive pigment was vermilion, at £3 15s.(?) a pound. This must reflect the relative unpredictability of verditer manufacture.

The blue glass pigment, smalt, is very transparent and its strength of colour, derived from the presence of small amounts of cobalt, is dependent on how coarsely it is ground. The coarsest grade of smalt, Hoegaerts's *stroyblauw*, was indeed more suitable to be strewn rather used in a paint.[208] The hue also varies; thus the pigment may be obtained in different degrees of coarseness and colour, varying from a strong purplish blue, close in colour to ultramarine, to a weak greyish blue. De Mayerne's list gave four grades and examples seen in seventeenth-century paintings vary considerably in colour. The smalt used as the underpaint in the sky of Van Dyck's *Equestrian Portrait of Charles I*, beneath a very thin glaze of ultramarine, is quite strongly coloured, whereas quite a grey-blue was used for the sky of *Lady Elizabeth Thimbelby and Dorothy, Viscountess Andover*. The strong colour of the smalt used in *Charles I* meant that ultramarine could be used very economically indeed, a point of some importance in a painting of this size. Van Dyck used smalt quite frequently, both for blue passages and in mixed greens of muted colour: it is found in the sky and, mixed with black and a yellow lake, in the discoloured foliage of the tree in *The Balbi Children* (see pp. 59, 62). Smalt is liable to discolour in oil medium, although often less so when mixed with lead white, and this has occurred in the foliage paint, where the oil medium has also darkened.[209] A greyish colour cannot always be attributed to this discoloration, however: sometimes smalt of this grade was chosen deliberately. A particularly pale grey, coarsely ground, smalt was used mixed with lead white as the underpaint for a stronger coloured blue paint in *A Distant View of a Town*, by Alexander Keirincx (London, Tate Gallery), an Antwerp painter who was employed by Charles I while in England in 1640–1.[210] The paint shows no sign of discoloration in this case and it must be assumed that this smalt was chosen for its cheapness.

Pigment mixtures

One of the most simple, economical, but effective pigment mixtures is that used to give purples and mauves. It was used for the child's dress in Van Dyck's *Portrait of a Woman and Child* (NG 3011), for the hanging in Rubens's *Samson and Delilah* (NG 6461, Plate 11 and Fig. 16), and for the mauve drapery of one of the figures in his '*Peace and War*': in each case it is composed of a mixture of red lake, lead white and charcoal black.[211] Few example of red lakes in the works of Rubens, Van Dyck or their contemporaries have been examined, but in the case of the red lake used for Charity's dress in Van Dyck's *Charity*, the dyestuff was extracted from the cochineal insect, probably the Mexican species, *Dactylopius coccus* Costa. The same lake is probably present in the red drapery on the figure of Peace in Rubens's '*Peace and War*', possibly mixed with a madder lake.[212] Cochineal dyestuff has also been identified in red lakes in the *Elevation of the Cross*.[213] Microscopic examination of red lakes in other paintings by Rubens or Van Dyck in the Collection suggests that a lake prepared from an insect dyestuff of this type is usually present, rather than the more orange-red madder lake.[214] Cochineal lakes are often a rather blue crimson, useful for purples and mauves; admixture with yellow gives a very much greater range of colours and red lake-containing glazes are frequently found to contain a yellow translucent pigment as well, often

Plate 11 Peter Paul Rubens, *Samson and Delilah* (NG 6461), *c*.1609. Detail of purple drapery, top.

Fig. 16 Peter Paul Rubens, *Samson and Delilah* (NG 6461), *c*.1609. Panel, 185 × 205 cm.

a yellow lake, occasionally an ochre. The cochineal lake was mixed with a yellow lake for the glaze on Charity's dress, although the yellow dyestuff present has not been identified; a yellow lake may also be present in Peace's red drapery.

Many mixtures are based on yellow, red or brown earth pigments; reds, for example, whether in an underpaint or in the principal paint layer, are rarely based on vermilion alone, but often contain a lake pigment or red ochre, or both. An example is Viscountess Andover's red-brown shawl in *Lady Elizabeth Thimbelby and Dorothy, Viscountess Andover*, which is painted in a mixture of all three types of pigment, with the addition of black. One reason for modulating the colour of vermilion is that it is very strong, dominating other colours to an extent that could be considered undesirable; in addition, many examples of vermilion seem to have been rather orange. Yellow ochre is very widely used, for clothing for example, often mixed with a yellow lake or other pigments: one example is Delilah's yellow cloak in *Samson and Delilah*; another is Viscountess Andover's dress, where the red iron oxide pigment haematite and other pigments are added to give a warmer, golden tone.

One of the most unobtrusively, but extensively used earth pigments in the work of both Rubens and Van Dyck is Cassel or Cologne earth. This translucent dark brown pigment gives depth of shadow in reds, browns and other colours: in Charity's dress in Van Dyck's *Charity* (see p. 66), for example, and the brownish areas in the dress of the old woman in *Samson and Delilah*. It is essentially an organic pigment, from lignitic or peat deposits, although it also contains an inorganic component, often the manganese-containing umber.[215] Its presence was indicated in some of the samples examined during analysis of organic components from the presence of a trace of fichtelite (see pp. 85–8). One of the translucent glazing pigments used by Van Dyck in England was a brownish birch bark tar. This was used in the background of *Lord John Stuart and his Brother, Lord Bernard Stuart* and to glaze shadows and folds on the sitters' clothing.[216] The same material was used to glaze the servant's yellow tunic in *William Feilding, 1st Earl of Denbigh* (see p. 85; Plate 44, p. 84). It was employed in the same manner as the asphaltum or bitumen identified in other pictures by Van Dyck or Rubens, or his studio. Those by Van Dyck include *Lady Elizabeth Thimbelby and Dorothy, Viscountess Andover*, *The Emperor Theodosius is forbidden by Saint Ambrose to enter Milan Cathedral* and the *Portrait of George Gage*; among Rubens's works it has been identified in the *Elevation of the Cross*.[217] Indeed, the birch bark tar was probably purchased as a bitumen-like material, rather than as a birch bark tar as such.

Van Dyck's and Rubens's palettes

If a comparison is made between the technique of Van Dyck and one of his predecessors in England, like Marcus Gheeraerts, whose technical background was similar, but who came from a generation earlier, there are similarities in the materials used. In Gheeraerts's *Portrait of Captain Thomas Lee*, painted in 1594, and *Portrait of a Woman in Red* of 1620 (Plate 12, both in the Tate Gallery, London), for example, the range of pigments is the same as that used by Van Dyck; the difference lies in the fact that, in Gheeraerts's work, the technique, with thin, carefully applied layers, meticulous brushwork and fine detail, is that of a late, but traditional, Netherlandish painter.[218] The author of MS Harley 6376 describes how a red lake glaze over a vermilion-containing underlayer should be blotted 'wth a little Lawne stuff^t wth cotten' to even it out; one can imagine a painter of Gheeraerts's generation doing this, but not a painter like Van Dyck (Plate 13).[219] Much of what is known about the materials and technique of Van Dyck's work in England relates to paintings produced in the manner Jabach described: a supremely well designed and controlled system of production in which Van Dyck provided the inspiration at the beginning and the breath of life at the end, but assistants did the ground work. In any discussion of the technique of painters like Rubens or Van Dyck, who organised their pattern of work so that it could be produced with considerable help from assistants, it is necessary to separate where possible the works for which the painter himself was largely responsible, and those in which studio assistants played a large part. In addition to this, some changes or developments over time, or with change of support or subject matter, may be expected. Van Dyck's studio was not on the same scale as that of Rubens, yet some of the pigment mixtures and techniques seen are closely similar and it seems likely that Van Dyck would have used much of what he had learnt during his time in Rubens's studio.

Van Dyck's *The Balbi Children*, painted in Genoa, shows a complexity and subtlety in the glazing of the draperies that is not seen in some of the later works painted in Antwerp, Brussels or London (see pp. 62–3). Such passages of painting embody a particular preoccupation in which the artist was absorbed at that time; one cannot imagine them being reproduced in a studio context. The annotations the artist made to his sketches during his travels in Italy studying the works of Titian, Veronese and others demonstrate his interest in the effects they achieved; his own

Plate 12 Marcus Gheeraerts the Younger, *Portrait of a Woman in Red*, 1620. Oak, 114.3 × 90.2 cm. London, Tate Gallery (no. T03456). Both dress and curtain are modelled in the underpaint layer using vermilion and lead white (with minor amounts of other pigments) in varying proportions; a red lake is present in the glaze paint (alone or with vermilion).

Plate 13 Anthony van Dyck, *Charity* (NG 6494), *c.*1627–8. Oak, 148.2 × 107.5 cm. Detail of red drapery, lower left. In the pinker areas the glaze paint contains a mixture of red and yellow lakes; Cassel earth is present in browner areas.

drapery construction derived much from a perceptive understanding of how the Venetian painters worked, but also from what he would have learnt from the sophisticated drapery painting technique of Rubens, shown, for example, in the painting of Delilah's crimson dress.[220] The layer structure revealed in many passages of paint, including draperies, in works by Van Dyck and Rubens where there was probably some studio assistance is often uncomplicated and economical: in the pigments chosen, but also in the fact that, by using a mixture of pigments to obtain the desired colour – red earth, vermilion, lead white and red lake, for example – it is easily and quickly modulated simply by adding a little more of one and a little less of another, without losing the overall unity of the passage. Much of the construction of the tonal values is done in this way in the underlayers, and although simple and ideally suited to work that is designed to be carried out in its preliminary stages by assistants (whether it was in practice or not), the effects obtained are often very subtle. This is partly due to the choice of pigments: for example, the use of ultramarine underpainted by mixtures of indigo

and white, and even mixed with indigo, in the dresses of Charity and the Virgin in *The Abbé Scaglia adoring the Virgin and Child*, and in various garments in Rubens's *Elevation of the Cross*.[221] Indigo was less expensive than ultramarine; it has a high tinting strength and, mixed with ultramarine, tends to counteract its slightly purplish tone. Mixed with lead white it gives a very flexible, easily worked paint, quite unlike smalt or ultramarine which are difficult to handle, although less so when mixed with white.

The technical study of the works of Van Dyck and Rubens in the National Gallery Collection has shown the supreme understanding they had of the properties and behaviour of their materials, without which they could not have delegated the work to others so effectively and could not have achieved such stupendous results. Roger de Piles, a perceptive critic of both Van Dyck and Rubens, declared that Rubens had a genius of the first order, but Van Dyck 'had the happiest pencil that ever any painter was blest with, Correggio only excepted'.[222] The technical study of their works has served to reinforce his judgement.

Acknowledgements

My thanks are due to Rica Jones of the Conservation Department, Tate Gallery, London, for invaluable discussion and assistance on technical information on paintings in the Tate Gallery Collection; to Karen Hearn, of the Tate Gallery, Penelope Rogers, of Textile Research Associates, York, Viola Pemberton-Pigott, of the Royal Collection, London, and Unn Plahter, Universitetets Oldsaksamling, Oslo, for useful discussions; and to Inge Schoups, Stadsarchief, Antwerp, and Dr Luigi Londei, Archivio di Stato, Rome, for helpful suggestions.

Notes and references

1. A.K.L. Thijs, 'Structural changes in the Antwerp industry from the fifteenth to eighteenth century', *The Rise and Decline of Urban Industries in Italy and in the Low Countries (Late Middle Ages – Early Modern Times)*, ed. H. Van der Wee, Leuven 1988, pp. 207–12.

2. J.A. van Houtte, *An Economic History of the Low Countries, 800–1800*, London 1977, esp. pp. 132–7, 162–6, 187–94, 204–10; J.I. Israel, *The Dutch Republic: Its Rise, Greatness and Fall, 1477–1806*, Oxford 1995 (1998 reprint), pp. 211–20, 242, 348–9, 410–20; A.K.L. Thijs, cited in note 1; R. de Peuter, 'Industrial development and de-industrialization in pre-modern towns: Brussels from the sixteenth to the eighteenth century – a provisional survey'; H. Soly, 'Social aspects of structural changes in the urban industries of eighteenth-century Brabant and Flanders'; H. Van der Wee, 'Industrial dynamics and the process of urbanization and de-urbanization in the Low Countries from the late Middle Ages to the eighteenth century – a synthesis', all in ed. H. Van der Wee, Leuven 1988, pp. 207–12; 213–40; 241–60, especially 241–2; 307–81, especially 342–55, cited in note 1; G. Martin, *National Gallery Catalogues: The Flemish School, circa 1600–circa 1900*, London 1970 (1986 reprint).

3. C. Brown, 'British Painting and the Low Countries', *Dynasties: Painting in Tudor and Jacobean England 1530–1630*; ed. K. Hearn, exh. cat., London 1995, pp. 27–31, esp. 30–1.

4. H. Peacham, *Graphice, or the Most Auncient and Excellent Art of Drawing and Limning Disposed into Three Bookes*, London 1612 (first published as *The Art of Drawing with the Pen* 1606), p. A2ᵛ. In this Peacham was echoing the sentiments of Sir Thomas Elyot writing some eighty years earlier in *The Boke Named The Governor* (London 1531), quoted by Brown 1995, p. 27. The Oxford English Dictionary defines a 'vauneant' (from the old French *vau-, vautneant*) as a good-for-nothing person. See also M.K. Talley, *Portrait Painting in England: Studies in the Technical Literature before 1700*, London 1981 (published privately by the Paul Mellon Centre for Studies in British Art), pp. 46–7.

5. Hearn 1995, cited in note 3, p. 202.

6. Hearn 1995, cited in note 3, p. 171.

7. M. Edmond, 'New light on the lives of miniaturists and large-scale portrait painters working in London in the sixteenth and seventeenth centuries' *The Walpole Society*, XLVII, 1978–1980, pp. 60–242, esp. pp. 84–9, 126–33.

8. J.B. van der Straelen, *Jaerboek der vermaerde en kunstryke Gilde van Sint Lucas binnen de Stad Antwerpen... (1434–1739)*, Antwerp 1855; Ph. Rombouts and Th. Van Lerius, *De Liggeren en andere Historische Archiven der Antwerpse Sint-Lucasgilde*, 2 vols., Antwerp 1864, The Hague 1876.

9. Rombouts and Van Lerius, II, 1876, cited in note 8, p. 61.

10. Rombouts and Van Lerius, I, 1864, cited in note 8, pp. 401, 443.

11. Rombouts and Van Lerius, I, 1864, cited in note 8, p. 514; R.-A. d'Hulst, *Jacob Jordaens*, Ithaca, NY, 1982, p. 28.

12. K. van der Stighelen, 'Young Anthony: Archival Discoveries Relating to Van Dyck's Early Career', *Van Dyck 350*; ed. S.J. Barnes and A.K. Wheelock, *Studies in the History of Art*, 46, National Gallery of Art, Washington 1994 (Center for Advanced Study in the Visual Arts Symposium Papers XXVI), pp. 17–46, esp. pp. 17–21; G.P. Bellori, *Le Vite de' pittori, scultori et architetti moderni*, Rome 1672, pp. 253–64, translation in C. Brown, *The Drawings of Anthony van Dyck*, exh. cat., New York 1991, pp. 17–23; Rombouts and Van Lerius, I, 1864, cited in note 8, p. 457.

13. Rombouts and Van Lerius, I, 1864, cited in note 8, p. 545; M. Rooses, *L'Oeuvre de P.P. Rubens: Histoire et description des tableaux et dessins*, 5 vols., Antwerp 1886–92, Vol. I, 1886, pp. 43–5; van der Stighelen 1994, cited in note 12; S.J. Barnes, 'The Young Van Dyck and Rubens', in A.K. Wheelock, S.J. Barnes and J.S. Held, *Anthony van Dyck*, exh. cat., Washington 1990, pp. 17–25.

14. Rombouts and Van Lerius, I, 1864, cited in note 8, p. 558, note 1, and p. 574.

15. E. Duverger, *Antwerpse kunstinventarissen uit de zeventiende eeuw*, Vol. 1. 1600–1617, Brussels 1984; Vol. 2. 1618–1626, 1985; Vol. 3. 1627–1635, 1987: Vol. 4. 1636–1642, 1989; Vol. 5. 1642–1649, 1991; Vol. 6. 1649–1653, 1992; Vol. 7. 1654–1658, 1993; Vol. 8. 1658–1666, 1995; Vol. 9. 1666–1674, 1997 (in progress); see Vol. 4, no. 1025, pp. 200–11, esp. pp. 208–9.

16. R.S. Magurn, ed., *The Letters of Peter Paul Rubens*, Cambridge, Mass. 1955; M. Rooses and Ch. Ruelens, *Correspondance de Rubens et documents epistolaires concernant sa vie et ses oeuvres*, 6 vols., Antwerp 1887–1909; see Magurn, no. 22, letter to Jacob de Bie, 11 May 1611, p. 55, Rooses and Ruelens II, 1898, CXXVIII, pp. 35–8; van der Stighelen 1994, cited in note 12, p. 21.

17. W.A.D. Englefield, *The History of the Painter-Stainers Company of London*, London 1923, pp. 66–73.

18. For the background to this see S. Foister, 'Foreigners at Court: Holbein, van Dyck and the Painter-Stainers

Company', *Art and Patronage in the Caroline Courts: Essays in Honour of Sir Oliver Millar*, ed. D. Howarth, Cambridge 1993, pp. 32–50. See also Englefield 1923, cited in note 17, for the proceedings beginning in April 1626, listing complaints against 'Strangers' and the plasterers, bricklayers, carpenters and other groups, pp. 94–7; complaint to the Lord Mayor in 1633 about the number of strangers in the city and their apprentices, p. 101; visit by the younger Robert Peake, a member of the Goldsmiths company, Richard Greenbury and others, all picture-makers, to the Company in 1634 and the 1636 proceedings of the picture-makers against strangers, pp. 101–2.

19. Englefield 1923, cited in note 17, pp. 94–105, Foister 1993, cited in note 18, pp. 32–3, 39–42.

20. Painter-Stainers Company Minute Book, 1623–1649, Guildhall Library MS 5667, f. 124, 22 November 1637.

21. Edmond 1978–80, cited in note 7, pp. 63–5, 215–19.

22. Edmond 1978–80, cited in note 7, pp. 137–40; W. D. Cooper, ed., *Lists of foreign Protestants and Aliens, resident in England 1618–1688, from Returns in the State Paper Office*, London 1882, p. 79. Gheeraerts, under the name of Marcus Garret, 'born at Bridges in Flaunders' is recorded to be 'picture-drawer to his Majesty, professing the apostolic faith taught and held by the Church of England K.J.'

23. Edmond 1978–80, cited in note 7, pp. 64–5, 124–6, 203, note 296.

24. Richard Symonds, who was in Rome between 1649 and 1651, described the large easel and benches used in the Academy and the lamp used to light it, saying that lamp light was best as it kept the shadows constant: see M. Beal, *A Study of Richard Symonds: His Italian Notebooks and their Relevance to Seventeenth-Century Painting Techniques*, PhD thesis, Courtauld Institute of Art, 1978, New York/ London 1984, p. 286. See also N. Pevsner, *Academies of Art, past and present*, Cambridge 1940, pp. 55–65.

25. According to Bellori they assumed from his fine apparel and refusal to join in that he held them in contempt; they were so rude about his work that he returned to Genoa: Bellori 1672, pp. 255–6, and Brown 1991, p. 18, both cited in note 12.

26. Pevsner 1940, cited in note 24, pp. 71–5, 80–2; see also G. J. Hoogewerff, *De Bentvueghels*, The Hague 1952, pp. 57–77. For the Utrecht academy see J. Bruyn, 'Rembrandt's workshop – function and production', C. Brown, J. Kelch and P. van Thiel, *Rembrandt: The Master & his Workshop: Paintings*, exh. cat., New Haven and London 1991, pp. 68–89, esp. pp. 68, 70, 87, note 17.

27. E. Norgate, *Miniatura or the Art of Limning*, ed. J. M. Muller and J. Murrell, New Haven and London 1997, pp. 108, 209–10, notes 306–7.

28. English documentary souces are discussed by R.D. Harley, *Artists' Pigments c. 1600–1835: A Study in English Documentary Sources*, 2nd edn., London 1982. For a survey, summaries and discussion of seventeenth-century English artists' manuals see Talley

1981, cited in note 4.

29. *Ricette per far ogni sorte di colore* (Padua, Biblioteca dell'Università MS 992, 16–17th century): M.P. Merrifield, *Original Treatises dating from the XIIth to XVIIIth Centuries on the Arts of Painting*, 2 vols., London 1849 (Dover reprint, New York, London 1967), Vol. II, pp. 641–717.

30. E. Hermens and A. Wallert, 'The Pekstok Papers, Lake Pigments, Prisons and Paint-mills', *Looking through Paintings: The Study of Painting Techniques and Materials in Support of Art Historical Research*, ed. E. Hermens, A. Ouwerkerk and N. Costaras, Baarn and London 1998, pp. 269–94, esp. pp. 280–7.

31. '*Traktaat om kleuren te bereiden*' (Antwerp, Plantin-Moretus Museum MS 253, sixteenth century): E. Vandamme, 'Een 16e-eeuws zuidnederlands receptenboek', *Jaarboek van het Koninklijk Museum voor Schone Kunsten Antwerpen*, 1974, pp.101–37. For a list and brief discussion of books of 'secrets' printed in Antwerp and in the United Provinces in the sixteenth and early seventeenth centuries see pp. 107–13; for later editions, largely from Dutch printers, see D. Bomford, C. Brown and A. Roy, *Art in the Making: Rembrandt*, exh. cat., London 1988, pp. 151–2, 154–5. See also W. Eamon, *Science and the Secrets of Nature: Books of Secrets in Medieval and Early Modern Culture*, Princeton 1994, pp. 112–33 on the *Kunstbüchlein* group and its successors, and pp. 139–47, 250–9 on Alessio Piemontese and the diffusion of his work through Northern Europe. An interesting late sixteenth-century English example in this tradition is Hugh Plat's *The Jewel House of Art and Nature: whereunto is added a rare and excellent discourse of minerals, stones, gums and rosins, with the vertues and use thereof*, by D.B. Gent, London 1653; first published 1594.

32. H. Peacham, *The Compleat Gentleman*, London 1622, pp. 110–17.

33. R. François [i.e. E. Binet], *Essay des merveilles de nature et des plus nobles artifices*, 9th edn., Paris 1632 (first published Rouen 1621), pp. 310–24. This is discussed in A. Massing, 'French Painting Technique in the Seventeenth and Early Eighteenth Centuries and De La Fontaine's *Académie de la peinture* (Paris 1679)', Hermens, Ouwerkerk and Costaras 1998, cited in note 30, pp. 319–90, esp. pp. 328–9.

34. P. Lebrun, *Recueil des essaies des merveilles de la peinture*, 1635, Merrifield 1849, cited in note 29, II, pp. 757–841. The parts equivalent to Binet's chapter appear on pp. 770–85, 805, 824–7.

35. C.P. Biens, *De Teecken-Const: ofte een korte ende klaere aen-leydinghe tot die lofelijcke const van teeckenen tot dienst ende behulp van de eerstbeghinnende jeucht ende liefhebbers, in elf capittelen vervat*, Amsterdam 1636; reprinted in E.A. de Klerk, '*De Teecken-Const*, een 17de-eeuws nederlands traktaatje', *Oud Holland*, 96, 1982, pp. 16–60. The text of the treatise was taken from a manuscript transcript appended to a study by C. Müller Hofstede in the Kunstmuseum, Basel; no

printed copy of the work appears to be extant.

36. T. Turquet de Mayerne, *Pictoria, Sculptoria, Tinctoria et quae subalternarum artium spectantia...*, 1620–46, British Library MS Sloane 2052. The earliest complete transcription was published by Ernst Berger in 1901: E. Berger, *Quellen für Maltechnik während der Renaissance deren Folgezeit (XVI–XVIII. Jahrhundert)*, Munich 1901 (Beiträge zur Entwicklungsgeschichte der Maltechnik, IV). See also the annotated edition by J.A. van de Graaf, *Het de Mayerne Manuscript als bron voor de schildertechniek van de Barok* (dissertation), Utrecht 1958; all references that follow are to this edition, cited as van de Graaf 1958, except where stated otherwise. See also Talley 1981, cited in note 4, pp. 72–149. For de Mayerne himself see H. Trevor-Roper, 'Mayerne and his Manuscript', *Art and Patronage in the Caroline Courts*, 1993, cited in note 18, pp. 264–93.

37. Norgate 1997, cited in note 27.

38. *The Art of Painting in Oyle by the Life*, British Library MS Harley 6376, ff. 86–109, cited below as MS Harley 6376. The first part of the manuscript, entitled *The Art of Limning, either by the Life, Landscapes, or Histories*, ff. 1–83, consists of a variant of the first version of Norgate's treatise on miniature painting (written 1627–8), with additional information from Nicholas Hilliard's treatise and perhaps from the author's own experience. Both parts are in the same handwriting and this section of the manuscript has the date '1664' appended, in paler ink, on f. 109. The manuscript could have been written soon after Van Dyck's death on 9 December 1641, as the painter is referred to in the past tense; see Norgate 1997, cited in note 27, pp. 25, 221. The author was trained in painting by 'Mr Wm. Martins the Elder' (see Harley 1982, cited in note 28, pp. 12–13); the suggestion by Jim Murrell in *The Way Howe to Lymne: Tudor Miniatures observed*, London 1983, pp. 59–61 that 'Martins' is an Anglicised form of Mytens, whose forename was Daniel, is unlikely. In this book it is also proposed that the author of MS Harley 6376 was the painter John Hoskins, who apparently trained as an oil painter and later turned to miniature painting. The section on oil painting bears some relation to that in *The Excellency of the Pen and Pencil*, London 1668, partly because both derived their information from sources close to Norgate, Peacham or John Bate's *The Mysteryes of Nature and Art, conteined in foure severall Tretises*, London 1633 (1634 reprint). It seems unlikely that Henry Gyles, the author of the later part of the manuscript, which is very different in tenor, had any intellectual responsibility for the content of those parts of the earlier section that are not derived from Norgate or other authors: see Harley 1982, cited in note 28, pp. 12–13.

39. R. Harley, 'Artists' Brushes – Historical Evidence from the Sixteenth to the Nineteenth Century', *Conservation and Restoration of Pictorial Art*, ed. N. Brommelle and P. Smith (papers presented at the International Institute for Conservation Lisbon Congress, 1972),

London 1976, pp. 61–6.

40. Magurn 1955, cited in note 16: on the drying of paint see, for example, nos. 30–2, letters to Sir Dudley Carleton, 20, 26 May 1618, pp. 63–6; no. 37, to Peter de Vischere, 27 April 1619, p. 70; no. 59, to M. de Valavez, 26 December 1624, pp. 99–100; no. 143, to Pierre Dupuy, 20 January 1628. pp. 230–1; on the yellowing of oil paint see no. 196, to Nicolas-Claude Fabri de Peiresc, 9 August 1629, pp. 321–3; no. 242, to Justus Sustermans, 12 March 1638, pp. 408–9; Rooses and Ruelens, cited in note 16, II, 1898, CLXX, pp. 161–4; CLXXIV–V, pp. 170–5; CLXXXV, p. 213; III, 1900, CCCLXVI, pp. 313–19; IV, 1904, DXXII, pp. 353–6; V, 1907, DCXVI, pp. 152–9; VI, 1909, DCCCL, pp. 207–11.

41. H. Vey, 'Anton van Dijck: über Maltechnik', *Bulletin van de Koninklijke Musea voor Schone Kunsten*, 9, 1960, pp. 193–201; see also English translation in Talley 1981, cited in note 4, pp. 150–5, and in C. Christensen, M. Palmer and M. Swicklik, 'Van Dyck's Painting Technique, His Writings, and Three Paintings in the National Gallery of Art', Wheelock, Barnes and Held 1990, cited in note 13, pp. 45–52, esp. pp. 45–6.

42. G. Adriani, *Anton van Dyck: italienisches Skizzenbuch*, Vienna 1965 (first published 1940), plate 108ᵛ; see also other colour notes on plates 8, 19, 50ᵛ–51, 59, 62, 104ᵛ. For the sketch after Veronese's *Allegory of Love, I* see plate 35ᵛ. For the notes on ingredients for varnishes see p. 35 and plate 121ᵛ.

43. M. Jaffé, *Van Dyck's Antwerp Sketchbook*, 2 vols., London 1966. For the recipes see Vol. 1, pp. 59–61, notes 111–18; Vol. 2, ff. 2ʳ–7ᵛ, pp. 205–16. For the place of the Antwerp sketchbook in van Dyck's *oeuvre* see Brown 1991, cited in note 12, pp. 38–47; J. Müller Hofstede, 'Van Dyck's Authorship Excluded – The Sketchbook at Chatsworth', in Barnes and Wheelock 1994, cited in note 12, pp. 48–60.

44. R. White and J. Kirby, 'Rembrandt and his Circle: Seventeenth-Century Dutch Paint Media Re-examined', *National Gallery Technical Bulletin*, 15, 1994, pp. 64–78, esp. pp. 68–9; Jaffé 1966, cited in note 43, II, f. 2ʳ, pp. 205, 210–11;

45. *Secreti diversi* (Venice, Marciana Library MS Ital. IV 48, 16th century): Merrifield 1849, cited in note 29, II, no. 403, pp. 634–5; *Ricette per far ogni sorte di colore*, Merrifield 1849, II, no. 48 pp. 670–1.

46. Van de Graaf 1958, cited in note 36, nos. 121–2, pp. 190–1. See also, for example, the remarks attributed to van Somer, no. 31a, p. 150. Jill Dunkerton has suggested that the sentence apparently referring to the blue glass pigment smalt in no. 122 (that it should be tempered at once with varnish and should not be overworked while wet) is ambiguous: the Italian word used, '*smalta*', in the feminine form, is incorrect; only the masculine form has ever been used. Also the verb '*smaltare*', usually used in the context of ceramics, could mean 'glaze' in the painting sense.

47. Van de Graaf 1958, cited in note 36, no. 86, pp. 177–8.

48. Talley 1981, cited in note 4, pp. 306–29.

49. Bellori 1672, pp. 263–4 and Brown 1991, p. 22, both

cited in note 12.

50. R. de Piles, *Cours de peinture par principes*, Paris 1708, pp. 291–3; see also Brown 1991, cited in note 12, pp. 34–5.

51. J. von Sandrart, *L'academia todesca della architectura, scultura e pittura, oder, Teutsche Academie der edlen Bau-, Bild- und Mahlerey-Künste...*, 2 vols., Nuremberg, vol. 1, 1675; vol. 2, 1679; Vol. 1, Part I, Book III, Chap. XI, pp. 80–1; MS Harley 6376, cited in note 38, ff. 86–7; see also ff. 6–7.

52. See also Norgate 1997, cited in note 27, p. 61 and note 41, pp. 125–6. MS Harley 6376, cited in note 38, suggests the grinding slab should be 18 inches square, f. 87.

53. Harley 1976, cited in note 39, pp. 61–6; L. Welther, *Die Geschichte und die Herstellung des abendländischen Künstlerpinsels*, Diplomarbeit, Institut für Technologie der Malerei der Staatlichen Akademie der Bildenden Künste, Stuttgart 1991; Norgate 1997, cited in note 27, pp. 66–7 and note 59, pp.130–2; see also pp. 225–6, 242–4, the latter from MS Harley 6376, ff. 12–16.

54. Duverger 3, 1987, cited in note 15, no. 776, 5 October 1632, pp. 313–14, for brushes and esp. p. 313 'een houten Manneken met sijn pedestael'.

55. Bate 1634, cited in note 38, title page to section on painting, and see Talley 1981, cited in note 4, plate 6; Harley 1976, cited in note 39, p. 65.

56. See, for example, the will of Frans Snijders and his wife Margaretha de Vos, Duverger 3, 1987, cited in note 15, no. 621, 20 September 1627, p. 70. His 'large grinding stone and the large easel' were bequeathed to Margaretha's brother Paul and 'the other grinding stone', an easel, palettes and brushes were bequeathed to Hendrick Rosiers.

57. Duverger 4, 1989, cited in note 15, no. 1016, 9 and 11 October 1638, pp. 183–90, esp. pp. 188–9.

58. Duverger 3, 1987, cited in note 15, no. 853, 6 February 1635, pp. 429–31, esp. p. 430.

59. Inventory of the property of Jasper Becx, Duverger 4, 1989, cited in note 15, no. 933, 26 March 1637, pp. 76–7, see p. 77. Antonio de Succa the Elder also had such a chest: see Duverger 2, 1985, cited in note 15, no. 363, 16 November 1620, pp. 143–5, esp. p. 144. For a discussion of the contents of studios in a Dutch context see C. Peres, 'Materialkundliche, wirtschaftliche und soziale Aspekte zur Gemäldeherstellung in den Niederlanden im 17. Jahrhundert', *Zeitschrift für Kunsttechnologie und Konservierung*, 2, 2, 1988, pp. 263–96. An example of a chest is illustrated on p. 282.

60. Duverger 4, 1989, cited in note 15, no. 1025, 4–5 November 1638, pp. 200–11, esp. pp. 208–9.

61. Duverger 3, 1987, cited in note 15, no. 639, 6–8 July 1628, pp. 103–11; see also J. Denucé, *The Antwerp Art Galleries: Inventories of the Art-Collections in Antwerp in the 16th and 17th Centuries*, Antwerp 1932, no. 17, pp. 47–51.

62. Martin 1986, cited in note 2, pp. 238–9.

63. A. Balis, *Corpus Rubenianum Ludwig Burchard,*

XVIII, *part II: Rubens Hunting Scenes*, London 1986, pp. 36–46; A. Balis, '"Fatto da un mio discepolo": Rubens's Studio Practices Reviewed', in *Rubens and his Workshop: 'The Flight of Lot and his Family from Sodom'*, ed. T. Nakamura, exh. cat., Tokyo 1993, pp. 97–127.

64. Magurn 1955, cited in note 16, letters to Sir Dudley Carleton, no. 28, 28 April 1618, pp. 59–61 with annotated list of paintings; no. 29, 12 May 1618, pp. 61–3; no. 31, 26 May 1618, pp. 64–6; Rooses and Ruelens, cited in note 16, II, CLXVI, pp.135–44; CLXVIII, pp. 149–60 (with description of studio); CLXXIV, pp. 170–4.

65. O. Millar, 'Van Dyck in London', Wheelock, Barnes and Held 1990, cited in note 13, pp. 53–8; R. de Piles, *Abregé de la vie des peintres, avec des réflexions sur leurs ouvrages ...*, 2nd edn., Paris 1715, pp. 403–8, esp. 404–7, for comments on slackness of workmanship in works Van Dyck painted towards the end of his life.

66. J. Wadum, 'A Preliminary Attempt to Identify Rubens's Studio Practice', *ICOM Committee for Conservation, 11th Triennial Meeting, Edinburgh, Scotland, 1–6 September 1996: Preprints*, 2 vols., ed. J. Bridgeland, London 1996, Vol. I, pp. 393–5.

67. Magurn 1955, no. 31, pp. 64–6. esp. p. 65; Rooses and Ruelens, II, CLXXIV, pp.170-4, both cited in note 64.

68. C. Brown, *Making and Meaning: Rubens's Landscapes*, exh. cat., London 1996, pp. 95–6.

69. Magurn 1955, cited in note 16, no. 8, letter to Annibale Chieppio, 24 May 1603, pp. 32–4; no. 45, letter to William Trumbull, 26 January 1621, p. 76; Rooses and Ruelens, cited in note 16, I, 1887, XXXI, pp. 144–50; II, 1898, CCXV, pp. 273–4.

70. The sketch for Rubens's *Samson and Delilah* (NG 6461) is on a softwood panel: see J. Plesters, '"Samson and Delilah": Rubens and the Art and Craft of Painting on Panel', *National Gallery Technical Bulletin*, 7, 1983, pp. 30–49, esp. p. 33 and note 9, p.47. See also J. Bauch, D. Eckstein and G. Brauner, 'Dendrochronologische Untersuchungen an Eichenholztafeln von Rubens-Gemälden', *Jahrbuch der Berliner Museen*, 20, 1978, pp. 209–21; P. Klein, D. Eckstein, T. Ważny and J. Bauch, 'New Findings for the Dendrochronological Dating of Panel Paintings of the 15th to 17th Century', *ICOM Committee for Conservation, 8th Triennial Meeting, Sydney, Australia, 6–11 September 1987: Preprints*, ed. K. Grimstad, 3 vols., Los Angeles 1987, Vol. 1, pp. 51–4; J. Vynckier, 'The structure of the supports', and 'Dendrochronological dating of the wings', *Peter Paul Rubens's Elevation of the Cross. Study, Examination and Treatment*, Bulletin de l'Institut Royal du Patrimoine Artistique, XXIV, 1992, pp. 55–7, 61–3.

73. Klein, Eckstein, Ważny and Bauch 1987, cited in note 70.

72. E. Schulte, 'Das Danziger Kontorbuch des Jakob Stöve aus Münster', *Hansische Geschichtsblätter*, 63, 1939, pp. 40–72, esp. pp. 44–6; A. von Ulmann, 'Über die Qualitätsbestimmung im Holzhandel. Ein Beitrag zur Materialgeschichte des ausgehenden Mittelalters',

Sculptures médiévales allemands: conservation et restauration. Actes du colloque organisé au musée du Louvre par le service culturel les 6 et 7 décembre 1991; ed. S. Guillot de Suduiraut, Paris 1993, pp. 223–32, esp. pp. 227, 232, note 9.

73. P. Klein, 'Some Aspects of the Utilization of different Wood Species in certain European Workshops', *Painting Techniques: History, Materials and Studio Practice: Contributions to the Dublin Congress, 7–11 September 1998*, ed. A. Roy and P. Smith, London 1998, pp. 112–14. From the second quarter of the seventeenth century, oak from regions other than the Baltic was used in Dutch workshops; Baltic oak was not used after 1650. In addition, wood of other species, European and tropical, was used more frequently.

74. T. Ważny and D. Eckstein, 'Der Holzhandel von Danzig/ Gdansk – Geschichte, Umfang und Reichweite', *Holz als Roh- und Werkstoff*, 45, 1987, pp. 509–13, esp. pp. 512–13. For England, Norway was already becoming a more reliable source of timber (principally pine); see S. Tveite, *Engelsk-Norsk trelasthandel 1640–1740* (dissertation), Bergen 1961. I am grateful to Unn Plahter for this reference.

75. Wazny and Eckstein 1987, cited in note 74, p. 511; H. Verougstraete-Marcq and R. Van Schoute, *Cadres et supports dans la peinture flamande aux 15e et 16e siècles*, Heure-le-Romain, 1989, pp. 76–8.

76. 'La Descente de Croix de Rubens. Etude préalable au traitement', *Bulletin de l'Institut Royal du Patrimoine Artistique*, V, 1962, pp. 6–187; the structure of all six large altarpieces is discussed on pp. 138–41; *Peter Paul Rubens's Elevation of the Cross. Study, Examination and Treatment*, *Bulletin de l'Institut Royal du Patrimoine Artistique*, XXIV, 1992.

77. J.A. Glatigny, 'The construction of the panels', *Peter Paul Rubens's Elevation of the Cross*, 1992, cited in note 76, pp. 57–61, esp. p. 58.

78. R. Lefève, 'La Descente de Croix de Rubens. Etude préalable au traitement. Les supports', *Bulletin de l'Institut Royal du Patrimoine Artistique*, V, 1962, pp. 128–45, esp. p. 134.

79. J. van den Nieuwenhuizen, 'La Descente de Croix de Rubens. Etude préalable au traitement. Histoire matérielle', *Bulletin de l'Institut Royal du Patrimoine Artistique*, V, 1962, pp. 27–85, esp. pp. 40–1.

80. R.-A. d'Hulst, N. De Poorter and M. Vandenven, *Jacob Jordaens (1593–1678), Volume I, Paintings and Tapestries*, exh. cat., Brussels 1993, pp. 134–7; Wheelock, Barnes and Held 1990, cited in note 13, pp. 201–3.

81. F. Baudouin, 'The Elevation of the Cross in Rubens's work', *Peter Paul Rubens's Elevation of the Cross*, 1992, cited in note 76, pp. 13–31, esp. pp. 13–15, and Rooses II, 1888, cited in note 13, pp. 79–81; A. Monbaillieu, 'P.P. Rubens en het "Nachtmael" voor St.-Winoksbergen (1611), een niet uitgevoerd schilderij van de meester', *Jaarboek van het Koninklijk Museum voor Schone Kunsten Antwerpen*, 1965, pp. 183–205: Doc. 2, pp. 195–6; Doc. 6, pp. 197–8; Doc. 12, p. 199; Doc. 25, p. 203; Doc. 26, p. 204.

82. Rooses II, 1888, cited in note 13, pp. 24–5.

83. J. Van Damme, 'De Antwerpse tafereelmakers en hun merken. Identificatie en betekenis', *Jaarboek van het Koninklijk Museum voor Schone Kunsten Antwerpen*, 1990, pp. 193–236: paragraphs 1, 2, 3, p. 235; 10, p. 236; for the two frame-makers see Rombouts and Van Lerius, I, 1864, cited in note 8, pp. 636–7.

84. J. Wadum, 'The Antwerp Brand on Paintings on Panel', Hermens, Ouwerkerk and Costaras 1998, cited in note 30, pp. 179–98, esp. p. 181; Nieuwenhuizen 1962, cited in note 79, doc. 3, p. 40; Lefève 1962, cited in note 78, pp. 129–31.

85. Duverger 3, 1987, cited in note 15, no. 615, 5–7 July 1627, pp. 30–62; see also Denucé 1932, cited in note 61, no. 16, pp. 39–47, but tools and household objects are not included.

86. Van Damme 1990, cited in note 83, paragraph 5, p. 235. The names of several *witters* are recorded in the Guild registers; see Rombouts and Van Lerius, I, 1864, cited in note 8, pp. 427, 454, 568, 571, 624–6, 632.

87. Rombouts and Van Lerius, I, 1864, cited in note 8, pp. 396–7, 402–3, Rooses II, 1888, cited in note 13, p. 177; N. Van Hout, 'Meaning and Development of the Ground Layer in Seventeenth Century Painting', Hermens, Ouwerkerk and Costaras 1998, cited in note 30, pp. 199–225, esp. pp. 200–5.

88. Duverger 3, 1987, no. 615, cited in note 85, p. 41.

89. Brown 1996, cited in note 68, pp. 100, 119.

90. Van Damme 1990, cited in note 83, paragraph 7, p. 236; Wadum 1998, cited in note 84, p. 182; Duverger 3, 1987, no. 615, cited in note 85; and many other inventories, for example that of the goods of Frans Franken the Elder, Duverger 1, 1984, cited in note 15, no. 247, 15 February 1617, pp. 389–94: *troniepaneelen*, *halffstooterkensmaeten*, *achtstuyversmaet*, etc.

91. J. Bruyn, 'Een onderzoek naar 17de-eeuwse schilderijformaten, voornamelijk in Noord-Nederland', *Oud Holland*, 93, 1979, pp. 96–115; Wadum 1998, cited in note 84, pp. 182–3.

92. Wadum 1998, cited in note 84, pp. 179–80, 183–90.

93. Van Damme 1990, cited in note 83, pp. 194–6 and para 4, p. 235.

94. Brown 1996, cited in note 68, pp. 95–101 and, with A. Reeve, pp. 116–21.

95. Rooses II, 1888, cited in note 13, pp. 173–80, esp. 175–7.

96. S. Alpers, *Corpus Rubenianum Ludwig Burchard, IX: The Decoration of the Torre de la Parada*, London 1971, pp. 36–8.

97. Magurn 1955, no. 43, letter to Duke Wolfgang Wilhelm of Neuburg, 24 July 1620, p. 75; Rooses and Ruelens, II, CCII, pp. 252–4, both cited in note 16. Rubens expressed his regrets that the paintings commissioned were too short for the ornamental frames already in place, even though he had been given the measurements in Neuburg feet and had had the framework on which the canvases had been stretched for painting constructed accordingly.

98. G. Bisacca and J. de la Fuente, 'Consideraciones

técnicas de la construcción y restauración del soporte de las Tres Gracias de Rubens', *Las Tres Gracias de Rubens. Estudio técnico y Restauración*, exh. cat., Museo del Prado, 16 April – 15 June 1998, Madrid 1998, pp. 51–66; Brown and Reeve in Brown 1996, cited in note 68, pp. 116–21. The structure of a number of Rubens's panels, some of them enlarged, is described in H. von Sonnenburg, 'Rubens' Bildaufbau und Technik, I: Bildträger, Grundierung und Vorskizzierung', *Maltechnik Restauro*, 85, 2, 1979, pp. 77–100, esp. pp. 78–83.

99. E. van de Wetering, 'The Canvas Support', in J. Bruyn, B. Haak, S.H. Levie and others, *A Corpus of Rembrandt Paintings*, Vol. II, The Hague/ London 1986, pp. 15–43, esp. pp. 15–19. This chapter has been updated in E. van de Wetering, *Rembrandt: The Painter at Work*, Amsterdam 1997, pp. 90–130; see pp. 92–6.

100. R.D. Connor, *The Weights and Measures of England*, London 1987, pp. 84–94.

101. L. Roberts, *The Merchants Mappe of Commerce, wherein the Universall Manner and Matter of Trade is compendiously handled ...*, London 1638, p. 37. He and other sources point out the common practice of making an allowance of about one inch a yard for errors during measuring and cutting.

102. Roberts 1638, cited in note 101, pp. 93–4; A. Martini, *Manuale di metrologia ossia misure, pesi e moneta, in uso attualmente e anticamente*, Turin 1883, pp. 223, 588. There were other palm units in Rome, including the *palmo mercantile* of about 24.9 cm, eight of which gave the *canna mercantile*.

103. J. Bastin, 'De Gentse lijnwaadmarkt en linnenhandel in de XVIIe eeuw', *Handelingen der Maatschappij voor Geschiedenis en Oudheidkunde te Gent*, 21, 1967, pp. 131–62.

104. The ell for white (bleached) linen was about 72.8 cm, and there was a third measure, the mercers' ell, of 69.8 cm which was very close to the Brabant ell of about 69.6 cm.

105. J.E. Thorold Rogers, *A History of Agriculture and Prices in England*, 7 vols., Oxford 1866–1902 (1963 reprint), Vol. VI, 1583–1702, 1887, p. 536: 1629 (Chatham) Ships' canvas: Vittery 1s 3d the ell. (Ipswich) 26s, 27s, a bolt. 1630 (Ipswich) bolt 27s. Vittery, ell, 1s 3d, 1s 6d, 1s 4d; Noyales, bale(?) £20, £19, £20 5s, £20 10s; yard 1s 6d. The French ell was equivalent to a little over 118cm, 118.2 cm before 1746. S.W. Beck, *The Drapers' Dictionary*, London 1886, 'Canvas', pp. 51–2. A charter of 1641 is cited, referring to various types of canvas, including 'French Canvas and Line, ell and half-quarter broad or upwards'; presumably the latter would measure about 50.6 inches or about 128.6 cm. Thanks are due to Penelope Rogers, Textile Research Associates, York, for this reference.

106. Van de Wetering 1986, p. 18, note 24; van de Wetering 1997, p. 95 and note 32, p. 299, both cited in note 99; *Letters and Papers, foreign and domestic, of the Reign of Henry VIII 1509–47*, ed. J.S. Brewer, J. Gairdner and R.H. Brodie, 21 vols., London 1862–1932, Vol. IV, part II, 1872, no. 3097 p. 1391, for 'Hollands' and canvas 'vetre vandalas'.

107. *The Rates of Merchandizes, that is to say, the Subsidie of Tonnage, the Subsidie of Poundage and the Subsidie of Woollen Cloathes or old Drapery, as they are rated and agreed on by the Commons House of Parliament ...*, London 1642, pp. 38–40, 55 for imported cloths, pp. 65, 75, 78 for exported. The first printed book of rates appeared in 1545; they were issued periodically thereafter. It is important to note that the monies listed are not the prices of the items, but the duties payable on them according to their estimated worth. It is unlikely that they were truly up-to-date in this respect, or entirely accurate in the list of imported items included, but they do give some idea of the range.

108. *The Merchant's Ware-house laid open, or, the Plain Dealing Linnen-Draper* (by J.F.), London 1695. Cloths discussed more or less alphabetically: canvases, pp. 5–6. The English cloth called canvas – and the name was properly given to the French textiles – was dyed yellow; it was described as better for stays than the French as it did not go out of shape; Holland, p. 1 onwards (the Amsterdam ell was equivalent to about 68.8 cm); burlap, p. 2; Ghentish Hollands, pp. 19–21; 'Frize' Holland, p. 17; 'Linnen – Hemp Roles', p. 23; 'Ozenbrucks', p. 32.

109. Talley 1981, cited in note 4, p. 366.

110. Thorold Rogers 1887, cited in note 105, p. 536: in the 1631 accounts of the Caryll family of Harting, Sussex, sixteen yards of 'feather bed tyke' were bought at 1s 2d a yard.

111. O. Millar, *Van Dyck in England*, exh. cat., London 1982, pp. 46–7. The main body of the canvas consists of two and a half strips of ticking, seamed vertically; personal communication from Viola Pemberton-Pigott.

112. E. Larsen, *The Paintings of Anthony van Dyck*, 2 vols., Freren 1988, Vol. I, pp. 325–7, Vol. II, p. 368.

113. D. De Jonghe and J. Vynckier, 'Eigenaardigheden in de weefselstructuur van sommighe dragers van 16de tot midden 18de eeuwse schilderijen uit de Vlaamse School', *Bulletin de l'Institut Royal du Patrimoine Artistique*, XXII, 1988/89, pp. 175–86, esp. pp. 180–1. I am grateful to Penelope Rogers for drawing my attention to this reference. The other paintings are *The Coronation of the Virgin*, painted by an unknown artist around 1635 (Mespelare, Sint-Aldegondekerk, 240 × 149 cm), and *The Son beheading his Father*, ascribed to Pieter Pieters and painted before 1614 (Ghent, Stedelijk Museum van de Bijloke, 247 × 215 cm). In 1610 Pieter Pieters was paid 11 pounds gross for supplying and making the painting, including the purchase of the ticking: see A. de Schryver and C. van de Velde, *Stad Gent, Oudheidkundig Museum, Abdij van de Bijloke. Catalogus van de schilderijen*, Ghent 1972, pp. 119–24, esp. p. 121. In the two representations of the *Coronation of the Virgin* the fibres have been identified as flax, spun with a Z-twist.

114. Martin 1986, cited in note 2, p. 133.

115. X. Henny, 'Hoe kwamen de Rotterdamse schilders aan hun verf?', *Rotterdamse Meesters uit de Gouden Eeuw*, ed. N. Schadee, exh. cat., Zwolle 1994, pp. 42–53, esp. p. 49 and notes 84–5, p. 53.

116. Tate Gallery Conservation dossier T02020. The painting measures 214.6 × 276.2 cm; the canvas is made up of three pieces. That used for the two larger pieces is a plain tabby weave; the third piece, used in the top left-hand corner, is a herringbone twill.

117. Martin 1986, cited in note 2, pp. 91–4; see also pp. 89–95 in this *Bulletin*.

118. Van de Wetering 1986, pp. 19–31; van de Wetering 1997, pp. 95–110, both cited in note 99..

119. Tate Gallery Conservation dossier T02139.

120. Tate Gallery Conservation dossier N02530.

121. Christensen, Palmer and Swicklik 1990, cited in note 41, p. 47.

122. Beal 1984, cited in note 24, pp. 85, 307.

123. P. Bagni, *Guercino a Cento: Le decorazioni di Casa Pannini*, Bologna 1984, p. 117 and figs. 96–7, pp. 126–7. The cultivation of hemp was one of the rural activities depicted in a series of landscapes decorating the Camera Rossa of the Casa Pannini, transferred to canvas in the nineteenth century and now in the Pinacoteca Civica, Cento. Guercino and two associates were commissioned to carry out the decorative scheme by Bartolomeo Pannini in 1615; it was completed in 1617. Guercino is thought to be responsible for the landscapes in the Camera Rossa. See also *Identificazione di un Caravaggio: Nuove tecnologie per una rilettura del 'San Giovanni Battista'*, ed. G. Correale, Venice 1990, pp. 48, 107.

124. P. Rogers, personal communication; see also van de Wetering 1986, note 23, p. 18; van de Wetering 1997, p. 94 and note 31, p. 299, both cited in note 99.

125. Van de Wetering 1986, pp. 31–3; van de Wetering 1997, pp. 111–16, both cited in note 99.

126. Such evidence may be seen in certain paintings where primary cusping may be seen on two opposite sides only: see Van de Wetering 1986, pp. 32–3; van de Wetering 1997, p. 116, both cited in note 99; see also Henny 1994, cited in note 115, p. 53, note 85 for rolls of primed canvas, for example '9 ells of primed canvas, two ells wide'.

127. Van de Wetering 1986, pp. 33–7; van de Wetering 1997, pp. 117–23, both cited in note 99.

128. J. Suckling, *The Works of Sir John Suckling – The Non-dramatic Works*, ed. T. Clayton, Oxford 1971, p. 121. A portrait of the poet, thought to have been painted by Van Dyck in about 1636–9, is in the Frick Collection, New York. The letter is thought to date from November 1631, or possibly 1637: given the proposed dating of the portrait and the fact that Van Dyck was not in England in 1631 the latter date seems more likely.

129. See the inventories of the property of Antonio de Succa the Elder and Joos de Momper, Duverger 2, 1985, no. 363, cited in note 59, p. 144; Duverger 3, 1987, no. 853, cited in note 58, p. 430.

130. Van de Wetering 1986, pp. 25, 30; van de Wetering 1997, pp. 109, 118 and notes 62–4, p. 302, both cited in note 99.

131. Van de Graaf 1958, cited in note 36, no. 6, p. 138; no. 40, p. 164. Much later, the author of *The Excellency of the Pen and Pencil* 1668, cited in note 38, commented that the work was troublesome so artists did not prime their own canvases, see p. 92.

132. Duverger 4, 1989, no. 1114, 21 July 1640, pp. 361–2, esp. p. 362; Duverger 5, 1991, no. 1383, 17 November 1645, pp. 263–86, esp. p. 277, both cited in note 15. Curiously, although the job of *witter* is listed in the guild regulations at this time, that of primer is not. It is not clear who would have stretched the canvases or primed them; it may well have been done by the frame- or panel-makers.

133. Duverger 3, 1987, no. 615, cited in note 85, pp. 39, 43; see also the inventory of the goods of Arnout de Bruijne the Elder, Duverger 3, 1987, cited in note 15, no. 778, 19–20 November 1632, pp. 315–19, esp. p. 316.

134. For standard-sized canvases in Holland, see van de Wetering 1986, p. 40, and van de Wetering 1997, pp. 125–6 and note 88, pp. 303–4, both cited in note 99; for Rome see Beal 1984, cited in note 24, p. 293; for London see Talley 1981, cited in note 4, pp. 284–5.

135. Magurn 1955, no. 21, letter to Johann Faber, 14 January 1611, pp. 53–4; Rooses and Ruelens, VI, 1909, CMXXXIV, pp. 327-31, both cited in note 16.

136. M.K. Komanecky, I. Horowitz and N. Eastaugh, 'Antwerp artists and the practice of painting on copper', Roy and Smith 1998, cited in note 73, pp. 136–9; I. Horowitz, 'Paintings on copper supports: techniques, deterioration and conservation', *The Conservator*, 10, 1986, pp. 44–8.

137. Peacham 1622, cited in note 32, p. 110; van de Graaf 1958, cited in note 36, nos. 1, 2, p. 135; MS Harley 6376, cited in note 38, ff. 94–5.

138. Plesters 1983, cited in note 70, p. 36, analysis by staining tests. For Van Dyck's *Charity* see p. 63 in this *Bulletin*; in this case the examination was by Fourier transform infra-red–microscopy. In Rubens's *Elevation of the Cross*, which has a thin grey priming containing lead white, charcoal and possibly chalk, the medium is described as oil and protein; see L. Kockaert, 'Composition and structure of the paint layers', *Peter Paul Rubens's Elevation of the Cross*, 1992, cited in note 76, pp. 63–77, esp. pp. 64, 77; microchemical tests were used for the examination. In the *Descent from the Cross*, examined in 1962 before more sophisticated instrumental methods of analysis were available, the medium of the grey priming was described as aqueous. See also von Sonnenburg 1979, part I, cited in note 98, pp. 85–7, where the medium is described as glue with added drying oil: the same limitations in analytical methods available apply here also.

139. Plesters 1983, cited in note 70, pp. 36–8, fig. 7, p. 34, fig. 14, p. 39.

140. Van Hout 1998, cited in note 87, pp. 205–7; here, *Naiads filling the Horn of Plenty* (The Hague,

Mauritshuis), which has a streaky priming, is attributed to Hendrick van Balen in collaboration either with Jan Brueghel the Elder, or Jan Brueghel the Younger. However, this has recently been attributed to the Rubens studio and Jan Brueghel the Elder: see J. Wadum 1996, cited in note 66. See also von Sonnenburg 1979, part I, cited in note 98, pp. 89–92.

141. Van de Graaf 1958, cited in note 36, no. 6, p. 138; MS Harley 6376, cited in note 38, ff. 95–6; Beal 1984, cited in note 24, pp. 87, 218–19.

142. Van de Graaf 1958, cited in note 36, nos. 6–17, pp. 138–41.

143. Beal 1984, cited in note 24, pp. 87, 218.

144. Millar 1982, cited in note 111, p, 46; O. Millar, *The Tudor, Stuart and Early Georgian Pictures in the Collection of Her Majesty the Queen*, 2 vols., London 1963, Text Vol., p. 98.

145. Plesters 1983, cited in note 70, pp. 33–4.

146. De Piles 1708, cited in note 50, p. 293; see also Brown 1991, cited in note 12, p. 35.

147. Brown 1991, cited in note 12, pp. 48–59.

148. Plesters 1983, cited in note 70, pp. 32–5.

149. S.J. Barnes, 'Van Dyck a Genova', *Van Dyck a Genova: Grande pittura e collezionismo*, ed. S.J. Barnes, P. Boccardo, C. Di Fabio and L. Tagliaferro, exh. cat., Milan 1997, pp. 64–81, esp. pp. 74–6. For the portrait studies see catalogue nos. 41–3, pp. 244–51; there is some doubt over Van Dyck's authorship of these studies. For the de Wael family and other Flemish painters in Genoa see, in the same catalogue, C. Di Fabio, 'Due generazioni di pittori fiamminghi a Genova (1602–1657) e la bottega di Cornelis de Wael', pp. 82–104.

150. Peacham 1612, cited in note 4, p. 82; H. Kühn, 'Verdigris and Copper Resinate', *Artists' Pigments: A Handbook of their History and Characteristics*, Vol. 2, ed. A. Roy, Washington/ Oxford 1993, pp. 131–58; Van de Graaf 1958, cited in note 36, no. 33, p. 152; 37g p. 162; Jaffé 1966, cited in note 43, II, no. 17, f. 4ʳ, pp. 207–8, 212–13.

151. Van de Graaf 1958, cited in note 36, nos. 34, 34a, pp. 152–3; 41, p. 164.

152. Van de Graaf 1958, cited in note 36, no. 23, p. 144.

153. Vandamme 1974, cited in note 31, p. 116; H. Kühn, 'Lead-Tin Yellow', *Artists' Pigments*, Vol. 2, 1993, cited in note 150, pp. 83–112, esp. pp. 83–91.

154. For a discussion of the preparation of synthetic blue and green copper-containing pigments see F. Ellwanger-Eckel, *Herstellung und Verwendung künstlicher grüner und blauer Kupferpigmente in der Malerei*, Diplomarbeit, Institut für Technologie der Malerei, Staatliche Akademie der Bildenden Künste, Stuttgart 1979. See also R.J. Gettens and E.W. FitzHugh, 'Azurite and Blue Verditer', and 'Malachite and Green Verditer', *Artists' Pigments*, Vol. 2, 1993, cited in note 150, pp. 23–35, esp. pp. 31–2, and pp. 183–202, esp. pp. 193–6.

155. M.V. Orna, M.J.D. Low and N.S. Baer, 'Synthetic blue pigments: ninth to sixteenth centuries. I. Literature', *Studies in Conservation*, 25, 1980, pp. 53–63; Harley 1982, cited in note 28, pp. 49–50.

156. Van de Graaf 1958, cited in note 36, no. 50, p. 170; nos. 51–62, pp. 170–3.

157. C. Merrett, *The Art of Glass: wherein are shown the Wayes to make and colour Glass, Pastes, Enamels, Lakes and other Curiosities*; translated from the Italian of A. Neri, London 1662, p. 292. Merrett's discussion of copper, brass and the production of verdigris, pp. 292–304, gives an indication of current understanding of the nature of the materials. See also Harley 1982, cited in note 28, pp. 50–1. See also Jaffé 1966, cited in note 43, II, no. 18, f. 4ʳ, pp. 208, 213.

158. P. and A. Mactaggart, 'Refiners' verditers', *Studies in Conservation*, 25, 1980, pp. 37–45.

159. J. Levy-van Halm, *Produktie en distributie van verfwaren in Nederland in de 17e eeuw*, unpublished thesis, September 1983. I am most grateful to the author for allowing me to consult her work.

160. Van de Graaf 1958, cited in note 36, no. 25, pp. 146–7.

161. Harley 1982, cited in note 28, pp. 119–20.

162. Beal 1984, cited in note 24, p. 197.

163. Harley 1982, cited in note 28, pp. 197–201.

164. Van de Graaf 1958, cited in note 36, nos. 91–7, pp. 180–2; for van Somer's instructions see no. 106, p. 185.

165. Van de Graaf 1958, cited in note 36, no. 106, p. 185; Mytens's recipes, nos. 111–12, pp. 186–7; see also nos. 98–9, 101–5, 107–8, pp. 183–5. For a brief discussion of the treatment of oil see White and Kirby 1994, cited in note 44, pp. 68–9.

166. Van de Graaf 1958, cited in note 36, no. 111, p. 186.

167. Van de Graaf 1958, cited in note 36, no. 113, p. 187; see also nos. 112, 114–20, pp. 187–90.

168. White and Kirby 1994, cited in note 44, pp. 68–9; R. White, J. Pilc and J. Kirby, 'Analyses of Paint Media', *National Gallery Technical Bulletin*, 19, 1998, pp. 74–95, esp. p. 81.

169. Van de Graaf 1958, cited in note 36, no. 86 p. 177.

170. J. Mills and R. White, 'The Gas Chromatographic Examination of Paint Media. Some Examples of Medium Identification in Paintings by Fatty Acid Analysis', Brommelle and Smith 1976, cited in note 39, pp. 72–7, esp. p. 76; J. Mills and R. White, 'Organic Analysis in the Arts: Some Further Paint Medium Analyses', *National Gallery Technical Bulletin*, 2, 1978, pp. 71–6, esp. p. 74; 'Analyses of Paint Media', *National Gallery Technical Bulletin*, 5, 1981, pp. 66–7; 'Analyses of Paint Media', *National Gallery Technical Bulletin*, 7, 1983, pp. 65–7; R. White and J. Pilc, 'Analyses of Paint Media', *National Gallery Technical Bulletin*, 16, 1995, pp. 85–95, esp. pp. 90–1, 95; R. White and A. Roy, 'GC–MS and SEM studies on the effects of solvent cleaning on old master paintings from the National Gallery, London', *Studies in Conservation*, 43, 1998, pp. 159–76, esp. pp. 166–7, 175; M. Van Bos, 'Materials and Techniques: The Binding Media', *Peter Paul Rubens's Elevation of the Cross*, 1992, cited in note 76, pp. 78–82.

171. White, Pilc and Kirby 1998, cited in note 168, pp. 74–5, 79.

172. White, Pilc and Kirby 1998, cited in note 168, pp.

76–7, 88.

173. J.S. Mills and R. White, *The Organic Chemistry of Museum Objects*, 2nd edn., London 1994, pp. 100–2. Fir balsam contains readily polymerisable components which improve the setting qualities of the resin. See also Jaffé 1966, cited in note 43, II, no. 18, f. 7ᵛ, pp. 210, 215.

174. Van de Graaf 1958, cited in note 36, no. 148, p. 203.

175. *Pharmacopoeia Londinensis in qua medicamenta antiqua et nova usitatissima, sedulo collecta ...* 3rd edn., London 1627, pp. 182, 204.

176. Talley 1981, cited in note 4, p. 325; information supplied to William Gandy by his father James, who worked in Van Dyck's studio; BL MS Harley 6376, cited in note 38, ff. 108–9, includes a recipe for Sir Nathaniel Bacon's Venice turpentine/ turpentine spirit varnish for oil paintings, also said to be used by Van Dyck 'when he did work over a face again the 2nd time all over, otherwise it will hardly dry'.

177. *The Rates of Merchandizes* 1642, cited in note 107; rates for 'drugges' and other pigments will be found in their alphabetical sequence, more or less.

178. T.D. Whittet, 'Pepperers, spicers and grocers – Forerunners of the apothecaries', *Proceedings of the Royal Society of Medicine*, 61, 1968, pp. 801–6; J.G.L. Burnby, *A Study of the English Apothecary from 1660 to 1760*, London 1983 (*Medical History*, Supplement no. 3, Welcome Institute for the History of Medicine), pp. 4–20, 53–5.

179. Edmond 1978–80, cited in note 7, pp. 177–8; Foister 1993, cited in note 18, pp. 36–7.

180. Van de Graaf 1958, cited in note 36, no. 25, pp. 146–7; the location of the other shop mentioned here is less easy to identify. The other shops include 'Mr Burthon's in Lothbery', near the Exchange, 'against the Stockes by the Fishmarket' (the north east end of Walbrook Street, roughly), and in 'Newgattmarket, at the Signe of the Tabard' (north of Saint Paul's Cathedral). See Berger 1901, cited in note 36, no. 185a, p. 250.

181. J. Stow, *The Survey of London ... completely finished by the study and Labour of A.M.* [Anthony Munday], *H.D.* [Henry Dyson] *and others*, London 1633. For the Popes Head alley area see pp. 209–16; 'Lothbery', p. 287; the 'Stockes Market for Fishmongers' (not Billingsgate), p. 243; for the pepperers, grocers and apothecaries in 'Cheape Ward', Sopers Lane and Bucklersbury, pp. 275–8; the quotation is from p. 276. For 'Port Poole or Grayes Inn Lane', where Fenn lived, see p. 486.

182. Trevor-Roper 1993, cited in note 36, p. 267.

183. Beal 1984, cited in note 24, p. 311.

184. W.F.H. Oldewelt, *Amsterdamsche archiefvondsten*, Amsterdam 1942, p. 154; Levy-van Halm 1983, cited in note 159, p. 12.

185. Rombouts and Van Lerius, I, 1864, cited in note 8, p. 304. In 1585–6, for example, those giving their profession as *kruidenier* included Michiel Quinet (Coigniet, Congnet) and Bastiaen Leers, p. 305. The former, who died in December 1623, was mathematician to Archduke Albert and his wife, Isabella, governors of the Spanish Netherlands.

186. The *Liggeren* registered Jan Bollaert as *schilder en apotheker* in 1557 and there are many other examples of members with more than one trade. Cornelis Nuyts was registered as a panel-maker in 1561, but a painter in the full accounts of 26 September 1585 to 30 September 1586, and a colour merchant in the full accounts of 6 October 1588 to 2 October 1589. See Rombouts and Van Lerius, I, 1864, cited in note 8, pp. 201, 225, 304, 338; for the colour merchants see pp. 305–7, 336–8, 340.

187. Duverger 1, 1984, cited in note 15, no. 114, 16 March 1609, pp. 201–6, esp. pp. 202–3.

188. Magurn 1955, cited in note 16, no. 42, letter to Hans Oberholtzer, 3 April 1620, pp. 74, 419, 445.

189. For the Delft dealer Frans Tobiasz. van den Bosch trading in colours see J. M. Montias, *Artists and Artisans in Delft: a socio-economic Study of the Seventeenth Century*, Princeton 1982, pp. 206–7. For the shop dealing in artists' materials and pictures opened by Leendert Henricx Volmarijn in Leiden in 1643, see W. Martin, '"Een kunsthandel" in een klapperman-swachthuis', *Oud Holland*, 19, 1901, pp. 86–8. See also Levy-van Halm 1983, cited in note 159, p. 22.

190. Duverger 2, 1985, cited in note 15, no. 359, 16 October 1620, pp. 139–40, esp. p. 140; no 579, 11 August 1626, pp. 477–83: for the value of the shop goods see p. 478; Lucas 'woonende totten schilder Ruebens', p. 481.

191. Spaegnaert's customers included Hendrick van Balen, Cornelis Schut and Arnout de Bruijne the Elder: Duverger 4, cited in note 15, no. 1066, 8 September 1639, pp. 273–7, esp. p. 275; no. 983, 25 February 1638, pp. 145–7, esp. p. 146; no. 922, 12–13 January 1637, pp. 56–60, esp. p. 60.

192. Duverger 4, 1989, no. 1016, cited in note 57, pp. 187, 190; Duverger 4, 1989, cited in note 15, no. 1051, 24 May 1639, pp. 250–2, esp. p. 251; see also A. Monballieu, 'Aantekeningen bij de schilderijeninventaris van het Sterfhuis van Jan Snellinck', *Jaarboek van het Koninklijk Museum voor Schone Kunsten Antwerpen*, 1976, pp. 245–68, esp. pp. 247–52, 260–1. Hans Snellincx, or Snellinck, the Younger is described as a colour merchant (perhaps working with his father?) in the 1621 inventory of the estate of Anna Vrolijck, widow of Hendrik Leunis and wife of Hubrecht Diericxs. de Clee, both painters, although by this time he was no longer living in Antwerp: Duverger 2, 1985, cited in note 15, no. 368, 8 March 1621, pp. 152–4, esp. p. 154; the debts to Hans Snellinck the Younger are listed among those outstanding from the estate.

193. Duverger 5, 1991, no. 1383, cited in note 132, p. 277; see also, for example, the payment made to the widow of Osias Beert, painter, for colours from the estate of Abraham Goyvaerts, 30 July 1629, Duverger 3, 1987, cited in note 15, pp. 162–5.

194. *The Rates of Merchandizes* 1642, cited in note 107, pp. 42, 74.

195. A. Roy and B. Berrie, 'A new lead-based yellow in the

seventeenth century', Roy and Smith 1998, cited in note 73, pp. 160–5. Naples yellow itself was used in Italy before any other country in Europe, rather later in the seventeenth century: see I.N.M. Wainwright, J.M. Taylor and R.D. Harley, 'Lead Antimonate Yellow', *Artists' Pigments: A Handbook of their History and Characteristics*, Vol. 1, ed. R.L. Feller, Washington/ Cambridge 1986, pp. 219–54, esp. pp. 223, 230–1.

196. Beal 1984, cited in note 24, p. 252.

197. Beal 1984, cited in note 24, p. 252; Van de Graaf 1958, cited in note 36, no. 32 p. 151; see also no. 22, p. 142.

198. C.A. Grissom, 'Green Earth', *Artists' Pigments*, Vol. 1, 1986, cited in note 195, pp. 141–67, esp. pp. 141–3, 148–9. The other, more common, variety of green earth is glauconite, also a clay mineral, but of sedimentary origin; celadonite is of volcanic origin.

199. Duverger 4, 1989, no. 1025, cited in note 60, pp. 204, 211.

200. J. Plesters, 'Ultramarine Blue, Natural and Artificial', *Artists' Pigments*, Vol. 2, 1993, cited in note 150, pp. 37–65, esp. pp. 37–41.

201. Rooses II, 1888, cited in note 13, p. 177.

202. R. de Piles, *The Art of Painting, with the Lives and Characters of above 300 of the most Eminent Painters, Containing a Complete Treatise of Painting, Designing and the Use of Prints ... to which is added An Essay towards an English School* [by B. Buckeridge], 2nd edn., London 1744, p. 361.

203. M. Rooses, *Jordaens: sa vie et ses oeuvres*, Amsterdam and Antwerp 1906, p. 131.

204. *Il libro dei conti del Guercino 1629–1666*, ed. B. Guelphi, Cento/ Bologna 1997, pp. 66–7.

205. Duverger 1, 1984, no. 114, cited in note 187, p. 202.

206. Van de Graaf 1958, cited in note 36, no. 25, p. 146; British Library MS Sloane 1990, f. 79r.

207. Depending on whether troy weight (used for pharmaceutical products) or avoirdupois was used, there were 12 or 16 ounces to the pound respectively; the troy ounce was equivalent to about 31g, the avoirdupois ounce 28.35g.

208. B. Mühlethaler and J. Thissen, 'Smalt', *Artists' Pigments*, Vol. 2, 1993, cited in note 150, pp.113–30, esp. pp. 113–16.

209. Mühlethaler and Thissen 1993, cited in note 208, pp. 116–20.

210. Tate Gallery Conservation dossier T04168.

211. See p. 55 and Plesters 1983, cited in note 70, pp. 45, 48–9; BL MS Harley 6376, cited in note 38, f. 92.

212. Analysis by high-performance liquid chromatography (HPLC), see J. Kirby and R. White, 'The Identification of Red Lake Pigment Dyestuffs and a Discussion of their Use', *National Gallery Technical Bulletin*, 17, 1996, pp. 56–80, especially pp. 67, 73; cochineal lake was used mixed with a madder lake in a painting by William Larkin: p. 67 and note 71, p. 79. The sample from 'Peace and War' was extremely small and the results were difficult to interpret. In some earlier investigations the presence of organic yellow or brown pigments may have interfered with

the examination of red lake dyestuffs. Analysis by thin-layer chromatography of the red lake used for Delilah's dress in Rubens's *Samson and Delilah*, which in some areas was mixed with a yellow lake (or similar material), and that present in the purple curtain suggested that they contained the dyestuffs extracted from the kermes insect and madder respectively. Recent examination of samples by microspectrophotometry suggests that a cochineal lake is probably present in both cases; confirmation by another method is necessary to rule out the presence of lac dyestuff. Thin-layer chromatography, together with microspectrophotometry, suggested the presence of cochineal lake in *Lady Elizabeth Thimbelby and Dorothy, Viscountess Andover*: see Plesters 1983, cited in note 70, pp. 39, 45.

213. J. Wouters, 'Materials and Techniques: Organic Lakes', *Peter Paul Rubens's Elevation of the Cross*, 1992, cited in note 76, p. 82.

214. Microspectrophotometric examination of samples from the red curtain in Van Dyck's *Woman and Child* (NG 3011) and from Silenus's armpit in the *Drunken Silenus supported by Satyrs* (NG 853), from the Rubens studio, suggests the probable presence of a cochineal lake in both cases. Distinction between cochineal and lac dyestuffs by this method is not clear-cut; confirmation of the results by another analytical method (HPLC) is forthcoming.

215. R. White, 'Brown and Black Organic Glazes, Pigments and Paints', *National Gallery Technical Bulletin*, 10, 1986, pp. 58–71, esp. p. 65.

216. White and Pilc 1995, cited in note 170, pp. 90–1, and note 24, p. 95.

217. Van Bos 1992, cited in note 170, p. 80.

218. R. Jones, 'Marcus Gheeraerts the Younger (1561–1635/6), *Portrait of Captain Thomas Lee* 1594', *Paint and Purpose: A Study of Technique in British Art*, ed. S. Hackney, R. Jones and J. Townsend, London 1999, pp. 26–31; Tate Gallery Conservation dossier T03456.

219. BL MS Harley 6376, cited in note 38, f. 102. Similar instructions are found in sixteenth-century sources: see J. Murrell, 'John Guillim's Book: A Heraldic Painter's *Vade Mecum*', *The Walpole Society*, LVII, 1993–94, pp. 1–51, especially p. 25: 'To Make a Red Rose'.

220. Plesters 1983, cited in note 70, p. 45. Rubens's painting methods are also discussed by H. van Sonnenburg, 'Rubens' Bildaufbau und Technik, II: Farbe und Auftragstechnik', *Maltechnik Restauro*, 85, 3, 1979, pp. 181–203.

221. Kockaert 1992, cited in note 138, p. 64.

222. De Piles 1715, cited in note 65, p. 390, 403; de Piles / Buckeridge 1744, cited in note 202, p. 267.

The National Gallery Van Dycks:
Technique and Development

ASHOK ROY

THE NATIONAL GALLERY'S holding of works by Anthony van Dyck is broad and substantial and represents virtually the whole of the artist's career and the variety of his production. In recent years five major paintings by him have been acquired: the double portrait of *Lady Elizabeth Thimbelby and Dorothy, Viscountess Andover* (NG 6437) bought for the Gallery in 1977, *Charity* (NG 6494) bought in 1984, with another acquisition made a year later, *The Balbi Children* (NG 6502), and the double portrait of the Stuart Brothers (NG 6518) acquired in 1988. Most recently, in 1997, the *Portrait of François Langlois* (NG 6567; Plate 1) was acquired jointly with the Barber Institute of Fine Arts in Birmingham. Details of these acquisitions may be found in the relevant National Gallery Reports. The works span Van Dyck's career from the early small-format portrait on panel of Cornelis van der Geest (NG 52), painted in Antwerp around 1620, to large and ambitious court portraits from England, painted in the late 1630s, including the monumental *Equestrian Portrait of Charles I* (NG 1172; 1637–8). Van Dyck's period in Italy (1621–7) is represented by two pictures: the *Portrait of George Gage with Two Attendants* (NG 49; probably 1622–3), likely to have been painted in Rome, and *The Balbi Children*, painted in Genoa in about 1625–7. There is also a work produced in Brussels: *The Abbé Scaglia adoring the Virgin and Child* (NG 4889; 1634–5) and, to represent Van Dyck's work as a designer of subjects for prints, there is an monochrome oil sketch on panel, *Carlo and Ubaldo see Rinaldo conquered by Love for Armida* (NG 877.2), also of about 1634–5.

The great majority of Van Dyck's paintings are in oil on canvas. The oil sketch on panel mentioned above is one exception; the other in the National Gallery Collection is a fairly large finished panel painting, as opposed to an oil sketch, of *Charity*, made in 1627–8 after Van Dyck's return to Antwerp from Italy. It is evident that a canvas painting technique suited Van Dyck's manner of working, both for portraits and for history pictures, since this

accorded most closely with the main works he had admired in Italy, particularly Venetian painting and, more specifically, the paintings of Titian, Veronese and Tintoretto. Working on canvas, as opposed to panel, in general allows greater speed of execution, the ready participation of studio assistants, and the production of paintings on a large scale at relatively lower cost. Furthermore, high-quality wood panels for painting are difficult to manufacture, particularly in larger sizes, requiring specialist carpentry skills as well as good supplies of high-quality timber. These were available in Antwerp, but perhaps less so in Italy and England during Van Dyck's periods there.[1] On panel, however, a higher degree of finish is possible, with smoother effects, and the rendering of refined detail becomes more attainable (Plates 2 and 3).[2] This explains the choice of panel for the oil sketch as a source for an engraving, where precision of representation is important. The use of panels for *modelli* to show clients is traditional, even if the finished work was to be on canvas, probably because the elements of design could best be emphasised in a small work on a support of wood. In *Charity*, which is painted on an oak panel, an unusually smooth paint surface was evidently sought to represent the vulnerable flesh of the naked children and to enhance the glossy, relatively high-key colour effects in the picture.

In most cases, other than in the works on panel, Van Dyck worked over a coloured ground of some sort, although in the paintings examined here, this seems rarely to have been very dark. Double grounds for canvas paintings are common at this period, and the upper ground was usually some shade of light brown, or light to mid-grey (Plates 4 and 5). Van Dyck seems to have been content to use the priming method in common currency in the country in which he was painting, and perhaps this indicates also the habitual use of ready-primed canvases from local sources of supply.

Other than a limited survey conducted in Washington in 1990,[3] little technical study has been

Plate 1 Anthony van Dyck, *Portrait of François Langlois* (NG 6567), 1630s? Canvas, 97.8 × 80 cm.

Plate 2 Van Dyck, *Portrait of a Woman and Child* (NG 3011). Detail of the woman's dress showing the application of impasto in a canvas painting. Compare Plate 3.

Plate 3 Van Dyck, *Charity* (NG 6494). Detail showing smoothly applied paint on a panel support.

Plate 4 Van Dyck, *Portrait of a Woman and Child.* Cross-section from the dark grey paint of the woman's dress. The double ground consists of a lower layer, largely calcium carbonate in oil, with a little earth pigment, and an upper layer of cool, light grey composed of lead white and wood charcoal. Original magnification 400×; actual magnification 240×.

Plate 5 Van Dyck, *Lady Elizabeth Thimbelby and Dorothy, Viscountess Andover* (NG 6347). Cross-section from Lady Dorothy's gold satin dress. The double ground consists of a red-brown lower layer of earth pigment and calcium carbonate with a warm mid-grey-brown upper layer. Original magnification 400×; actual magnification 240×.

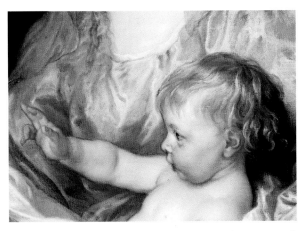

Plate 6 Van Dyck, *The Abbé Scaglia adoring the Virgin and Child* (NG 4889). Detail showing outlining in tones of red and brown paint.

made on Van Dyck's paintings, although there is no reason to suspect that they would depart in any significant way in materials and methods of painting from standard practice of the period. As Jo Kirby has explained in her article above, that practice has been recorded to some extent by Theodore de Mayerne, but it is unclear whether his accounts, notes and commentaries are always accurate or well-understood. But there is no doubt that de Mayerne's record is a very valuable one generally for seventeenth-century painting technique, and particularly for the materials in use. The methods Van Dyck specifically employs can often be evaluated best by close examination of the paint surface: the free and frequently open brushwork allows underpaints to be glimpsed through dragged surface paints, underdrawing in fluid dark paint can sometimes be seen at the junctions of passages of paint where these do not quite meet and outlines are often reinforced (Plate 6). The range of pigments employed, judged through the stereomicroscope, is neither particularly elaborate nor unusual. The technical characteristics of the paintings can be ascertained by a combination of visual examination and photography, or imaging with X-rays and infra-red radiation. Any remaining questions can usually be answered by analysis of samples, and examination of layer structure by standard methods.[4]

Many of the National Gallery Van Dycks have been subject to a certain amount of technical scrutiny over the years, usually in connection with questions raised in advance of, or during, conservation treatment. This information has not been gathered in a highly systematic way, but there is sufficient technical material, and the pictures are sufficiently diverse in subject matter and date, to justify a survey of Van Dyck's paintings. This survey, arranged chronologically, is presented below for all the paintings which have undergone at least some analysis. Further information on condition, subject matter, history and provenance is given in Gregory Martin's *Catalogue of the Flemish School*.[5]

Portrait of a Woman and Child

Canvas, plain weave (tabby): 13↕ × 12↔ threads/cm;[6] 131.5 × 106 cm.

This double portrait (Plate 7) is thought to have been painted in 1620 or 1621, either in Antwerp just before Van Dyck's departure to Italy in 1621, or on his arrival in Genoa that year. It is just possible that the picture dates from a visit to London in 1620. The materials and technique of the picture seem more in accord with an Antwerp origin than one in Genoa, since Van Dyck's Genoese portraits appear generally to have single-layered light or mid-brown grounds.[7] The ground of the present painting consists of two layers: a semi-translucent lower layer, largely calcium carbonate, but containing also a little red and brown ochre bound in a drying oil, over which there is a warm mid-grey oil paint, mainly of lead white, with wood charcoal and some brownish ochre. Canvas grounds of this general type were standard in Antwerp and elsewhere in the Low Countries from the early seventeenth century, and are found in paintings by Rubens, Jordaens, Frans Snijders, David Teniers and others. In the *Woman and Child* this ground is substantially concealed by the overlying layers of paint, and it plays little role in the composition or the colour design of the picture, although it can just be seen through thin wash-like paint beneath the child's chin and cheek at the junction with the small lace ruff, at the woman's temple, where the paint is exceedingly thin, and between the brushwork of the impasto touches of the lace at the woman's cuff. In contrast to some of Van Dyck's later works, particularly from the 1630s, the forms meet one another tightly, concealing the ground that might otherwise be visible at the junctions.

It is evident from close examination of the picture's surface, from an infra-red photograph and from several paint cross-sections that a certain amount of free underdrawing in a dark translucent paint was used over the ground to mark out the central forms. This can be seen particularly in the outline of the child's head, nose, profile of the lips and around the fingers, and marking out the top of the woman's head and hairband, at her chin and

Plate 7 Anthony van Dyck, *Portrait of a Woman and Child* (NG 3011), *c*.1620–1. Canvas, 131.5 × 106 cm.

Fig. 1 Van Dyck, *Portrait of a Woman and Child*. X-ray detail of the child showing the application of lead white in the flesh tones, sleeve and child's ruff.

Plate 8 Van Dyck, *Portrait of a Woman and Child*. Detail of the child's head.

around her ear. The infra-red photograph and paint sections suggest underdrawing, in dark lines of paint, beneath the background curtain, and there are shaded areas under the woman's embroidered bodice. Infra-red light also reveals a dark, nebulous, roughly rectangular patch beneath the curtain just above the woman's head, suggesting one of the few changes in composition made during the course of execution. The underdrawing material consists of a dark translucent brown pigment such as an umber or Cassel earth. Analysis by EDX confirmed the presence of manganese as well as iron in this material and this result agrees with a neutron autoradiographic study carried out in New York by the Metropolitan Museum on a painting by Van Dyck of *c.*1624.[8] Dark shading beneath the purple dress in the darkest folds below the child's left arm consists of wood charcoal, while in other pictures bone black has been detected in underdrawing and shading.[9]

The manner of application of the paint layers is probably best judged from the picture itself, since the method of painting is straightforward and direct. X-ray photographs show the constructive brushwork in paint containing large amounts of lead white for the flesh tones, the lace ruffs, the white cloth clutched by the child and the underlayers and highlights of the purple dress (Fig. 1). As with the infra-red image, the composite X-ray photograph shows only the most minor changes of design as the painting proceeded.

Such changes in design as can be detected are confined to some adjustment of the angle of the woman's head, to the pattern of her embroidered bodice and to the precise positioning of the child's outstretched hand.

The palette and layer structure of the picture have been examined in samples and cross-sections and by EDX and XRD analysis. The range of materials employed is not large and proves to be quite standard for the seventeenth century. Subtlety of colour and colour design relies on pigment mixtures and the multi-layered application of paint, and is perhaps most elaborate in the child's purple dress and in the deep red of the background curtain. The flesh tones, which have a dragged, rather desiccated-looking texture, consist principally of lead white, tinted lightly with vermilion to give a pale pure pink tone grading into half shadow produced by the addition of earth pigments (Plate 8). The faintly cool tones of the child's cheek to the left are provided by mineral azurite scumbled over the pink, and similar effects appear to have been used in the woman's face. The whites of the child's eyes are tinged with blue, probably azurite.

Natural azurite, with other pigments, principally small amounts of black, white and a brownish ochre, form the blues and greens of the background landscape, while the dull grey-blue of the sky is composed of pure smalt, and smalt with white and black, with the more grey-blues passing over a grey underpaint in places.

In their manner of execution, the draperies are the most elaborate parts of the picture. The deep crimson curtain framing the sitters is made up of up to five layers of partly blended paint based on vermilion and a deep claret-coloured lake, with black incorporated in the deepest shadows. A red-brown earth is also used (Plate 9). The vermilion is present in two forms: a very finely ground, orange-toned variety and a brighter scarlet type consisting of larger, more angular, particles. With these combinations of pigments and a sequence of layers, a considerable range as well as depth of colour is achieved. Except in the shadows, where the underlayers are red lake with black, the lowermost layer of the curtain is virtually pure orange-coloured vermilion. The final layer is the most glaze-like in constitution and is largely red lake, but there are also highlights of vermilion used at the surface, such as at the fringed edge picked out in opaque bright red pigment to the left and repeated in the small swathe of textile above the child's head. Van Dyck's interest in, and success in, depicting the colours, textures and shine of textiles had clearly developed by this early point in his career: the draperies of the sitters are painted with particular verve and skill. Detail was also important to Van Dyck since he incorporates into the brilliantly executed network of lace at the woman's cuff a few vermilion cross-threads, only visible at close quarters. The woman's black dress combines deep charcoal-black pigment with cool mixed greys and the addition of a small amount of deep red lake to the black pigment in the darks imparts a glossy rich depth. The embroidered brown and gold of the woman's bodice contains ochres and white with occasional dashed highlight touches of lead-tin yellow;[10] the bands of similar colour around the child's upper arms must have been worked in an equivalent way and recall the brilliant effects of embroidered textiles seen in *Susanna Fourment and her Daughter* of about the same date in Washington (National Gallery of Art).[11]

Perhaps the most striking and unusual colour in the painting as a whole is the child's beautiful purple satin dress. The colour varies from almost pure black in the shadow beneath the right arm to pale lilac lights on the folds of the fabric. Mauves and purples were difficult to obtain from the seventeenth-century palette except by mixing, since no pure purple-coloured pigment was available for oil painting. A successful colour could be obtained by combining ultramarine with red lake, with or without white, or by glazing one over the other, but at considerable

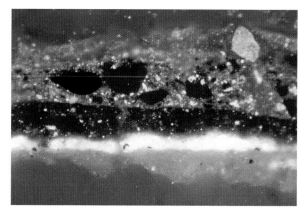

Plate 9 Van Dyck, *Portrait of a Woman and Child*. Cross-section of the red of the curtain with multiple applications of paint containing vermilion, red lake pigment and earth pigments. The double ground is visible beneath. Original magnification 400×; actual magnification 320×.

Plate 10 Van Dyck, *Portrait of a Woman and Child*. Top surface of the paint of the child's purple dress containing lead white, red lake and charcoal black. Original magnification 275×; actual magnification 220×.

expense on account of the ultramarine content. Azurite combined with red lakes tends to make more muted greyish mauves. Here Van Dyck uses instead a mixture of varying proportions of white, a red lake and charcoal black[12] over, in the mid-tones and lights, an underpaint of a pure reflective lead white. The specific optical properties of the pigments – as a result of their reflectance and absorption characteristics when combined – yield the strong purple and mauves seen in this drapery (Plate 10), particularly since a light-reflecting layer is present beneath. This technique and the resulting colour had been exploited with considerable success by Rubens in his large panel of *Samson and Delilah* in the National Gallery (NG 6461; *c.*1609), in which the same combination of pigments occurs in the great swag of purple drapery framing the upper left part of the composition.[13]

Plate 11 Anthony van Dyck, *Portrait of George Gage with Two Attendants* (NG 49), probably 1622–3. Canvas, 115 × 113.5 cm.

Portrait of George Gage with Two Attendants
Canvas, overall 115 × 113.5 cm (for thread counts, see text).

This picture (Plate 11) presents a particular problem of interpretation, since it has undergone a significant modification at the right side, where an irregularly shaped strip of canvas, about 21 cm wide at the top and 18 cm at the bottom, has been sewn on to the main piece of canvas. A smaller rectangular addition, also sewn on, makes up the lower right-hand corner (roughly 19 × 8 cm). In his 1970 Catalogue, Martin

speculated that the picture was painted by an unknown artist after a Van Dyck portrait, citing weaknesses in design and execution while acknowledging the problematic condition of the picture.[14] More recent opinion, summarised by Susan Barnes in her catalogue entry for the 1990–1 Van Dyck exhibition held in Washington (National Gallery of Art), reconfirmed the identification of the

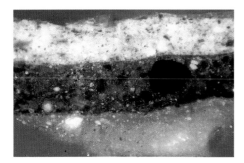

Plate 12 Van Dyck, *Portrait of George Gage with Two Attendants*. Cross-section of blue-grey sky, upper right, on main portion of canvas. The lower two layers of translucent brownish orange and thin grey paints represent the double ground. Under the sky paint there is a dark purple layer, probably a pentimento in the background. Original magnification 220×; actual magnification 135×.

Plate 13 Van Dyck, *Portrait of George Gage with Two Attendants*. Cross-section of the grey-blue paint of the right-hand figure's sleeve, just to the left of the canvas join, showing the double ground on the main canvas and a thick layer of new grey ground over this. The new ground overlaps the seam from the right-hand canvas addition. Original magnification 155×; actual magnification 100×. (See also Fig. 4.)

main sitter as George Gage, first made by Millar, although rejected by Martin, and concluded that the painting was an autograph Van Dyck, probably painted in Rome, rather than in Antwerp or in England, between 1622 and 1623.[15] The subject is explained by Gage's activities as an agent for Sir Dudley Carleton's art collection, and he was in Rome at the same time as Van Dyck, probably overlapping by eleven months.

X-ray photographs show the sewn right-hand addition very clearly, and also differences in radiographic density between the main part of the composition; but the images of the paint layers, both at the surface and beneath, are difficult to read and ascribe to parts of the composition, visible or concealed . Thread counts of the two canvases made on the radiographic images show the main part to be a finer canvas than the sewn addition (16 × 18 threads/cm as compared to 13 × 14 threads/cm). Cross-sectional samples on either side of the join are of help in establishing the sequence of the grounds and paint layers, and therefore in the interpretation of the evolution of the composition, but there remain questions which cannot be resolved with certainty. It is clear from these technical studies that the addition was not attached before the canvas assemblage was primed for painting: the ground layers on each piece differ. Those on the main portion consist of a somewhat translucent lower ground of a mid red-brown, and over this a thin layer of grey comprising lead white, lampblack and calcium carbonate (Plates 12 and 13).[16] On the added strip there is also a two-layered system, fairly similar in colour, but markedly different in constitution, thickness and texture. A coarse-grained carbon black is present in the upper

grey ground here, while the lower brown layer is a mixture of earth pigments only, resulting in an optically denser priming on the addition.

Examination of the paint layers on each side of the joined canvas suggests that the main part of the painting bearing the figure of George Gage was cut at the right side at an advanced stage in the painting and the addition applied subsequently. The main piece of evidence for this is that the head of the right-hand figure was present before the composition was cut, since the paint layers for the front part of his face – the forehead, part of the eye and nose – come to an abrupt end at the seam joining the two canvases (Figs. 2 and 3). Similar observations can be made for other parts of the present composition in the region of the join, particularly in the grey-blue sleeve of the right-hand figure where the hand, arm and sleeve must always have been present on the main canvas. The X-ray photographs indicate that after the addition had been applied, there was a certain amount of scraping away of paint to the left of the join and ground to the right, followed by the application of a patch of new, relatively thick, grey ground to conceal the seam and prepare the addition for extension of the composition over the join. This ground consists of a mixture of pigments, principally white with a fine-grained black, but also some red lead, small quantities of azurite, red lake and other pigments; it is therefore unlike either of the two earlier grey ground layers on the two joined pieces of canvas (Plate 13).[17] The layer of grey paint forming the new ground is visible in the X-ray as an irregular strip, about 6–9 cm wide, running along the length of the seam, but spreading out beneath the thin paint of the main part of the right-hand figure's head and beneath the antique statue

Fig. 2 Van Dyck, *Portrait of George Gage with Two Attendants.* Detail of the seam passing through the face of the figure at the right.

Fig. 3 Van Dyck, *Portrait of George Gage with Two Attendants.* X-ray detail showing the seam joining the right-hand canvas addition. Part of the profile of the figure at the right is just visible to the left of the seam.

both on the added strip and under the legs of the statue on the main canvas (Fig. 4). Examination of cross-sections suggests that there may have been paint as well as priming layers on the addition, although evidently not an extensive or complete composition. For example an irregular oval area of vermilion and red lake, on the addition, underlies the right-hand man's yellow-brown cloak around his shoulder, but bears no relation in form to the paint on top. Similarly a layer containing azurite is present beneath the thigh of the marble statue on the addition.

The sequence of events that might explain these features can be summarised as follows. Van Dyck painted the portrait of George Gage with the two other figures, probably art dealers, with whom it is suggested he is in negotiation. The original format cannot be known, nor can the reason for its cutting down. An extra strip of canvas, already grounded and probably also bearing some incomplete part of a painting, was then sewn on to the main canvas after some partial scraping of the paint layers and ground at the two edges to be joined. A new grey ground was applied over the join, around the profile of the right-hand man's head on the main canvas and under what is now the statue. The right-hand figure was then completed and further finishing touches to unite

the two portions applied over the seam. This was presumably carried out very soon after, since the new ground was apparently still either wet, or soft enough to merge with the paint layers on top, in spite of its strongly siccative constitution.[18]

There were clearly some modifications made to the detail of the earlier design. The X-ray image indicates alterations to Gage's head, particularly the direction of his gaze. Further, it is not certain that the object being displayed for consideration was always a statue, since only brownish and greyish-white drapery was present on the main canvas and the legs of the sculpture appear to have been constructed after the addition had been sewn on. The change in the right-hand man's hand to include the middle finger as well as the thumb pointing to, or grasping, the object on offer may be a late change and possibly also the reworking of Gage's sleeve and cuff to the left. The background to the main sitter may also have been recast somewhat, and there is evidence for an incomplete curtain occupying the upper part of the composition beneath the classical columns: a layer of deep purple paint lies beneath the patch of sky to the right of Gage's head, where there are also signs of late alteration to the architectural setting.

Owing to this complexity, the portrait of George

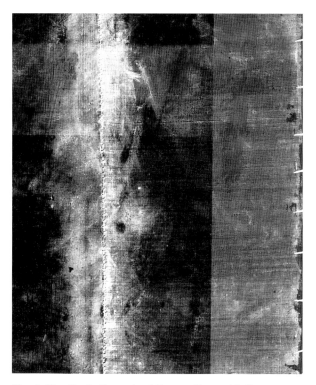

Fig. 4 Van Dyck, *Portrait of George Gage with Two Attendants*. X-ray detail of another section of the seam showing the application of new X-ray-dense ground over the join.

Gage does not present a straightforward example of Van Dyck's technique, although there are other cases of his re-use of canvases and major modification of design at this period in his career, notably the large-scale canvas of *Saint Martin dividing his Cloak*, *c*.1620, in the Royal Collection (Windsor).[19] The painting of George Gage, however, remains extraordinary for its unusual and innovative subject, which Van Dyck, it appears, had considerable difficulty in crystallising.

The Balbi Children

Canvas, plain weave (tabby), 11↕ × 8↔ threads/cm; 219 × 151 cm.

The sitters are from an aristocratic Genoese family, traditionally thought to be the Balbi, from whom Van Dyck received a number of portrait commissions, but there is no certain identification of the three children; however, this title is retained here. The picture, painted in Genoa between 1625 and 1627 (Plate 15), is on a single piece of coarse canvas, in which a number of prominent weave faults are present. No seams or joins are visible in the X-ray of the picture. The format is similar to a number of Van Dyck's portraits from Genoa, including, for example, '*La Dama d'Oro', Battina Balbi (?) with Two of her*

Children (*c*.1622, canvas 218 × 146 cm; Genoa, Palazzo Durazzo Pallavicini), *Agostino Pallavicini* (*c*.1622, canvas 216 × 141 cm; Los Angeles, J. Paul Getty Museum), and *A Genoese Noblewoman with her Child* (*c*.1623–5, canvas 218 × 146 cm; Cleveland Museum of Art). *Marchesa Balbi*, *c*.1622, in Washington (National Gallery of Art), however, is somewhat smaller (canvas, 183 × 122 cm).[20]

The ground of the National Gallery picture consists of a single layer of a brownish-cream colour, composed principally of calcium carbonate and silica (silicon dioxide) bound in oil. There are also small amounts of brownish earth and lead white present, but the main component may be a pulverised silaceous limestone or similar deposit (Plate 14).[21] This constitution for a priming is fairly common in seventeenth-century canvas painting both in Italy and Spain and must be regarded as standard practice in a number of locations, particularly in the earlier part of the seventeenth century.[22] There is reason to suspect that the ground now appears darker than when it was originally applied, and this seems to be a general phenomenon for grounds of this type. The various materials that make up the ground are relatively translucent in oil and become more so with age, allowing the colour of the darkened glue size on the canvas beneath to exert an effect. Traditional lining methods and the adhesives used would have exacerbated darkening, as would the retention of old, darkened varnish residues within a relatively absorbent priming. In the *Balbi Children*, large areas of ground in the background setting, the architecture and foreground, are either left unpainted to stand for the mid-tones, or are covered by only the thinnest wash of paint. Since the present varnish on the

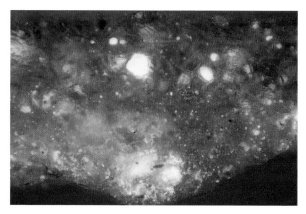

Plate 14 Van Dyck, *The Balbi Children*. Cross-section of the sky paint, upper left, showing severely deteriorated smalt. The translucent grey-brown ground is visible beneath. Original magnification 275×; actual magnification 165×.

59

Plate 15 Anthony van Dyck, *The Balbi Children* (NG 6502), *c.*1625–7. Canvas, 219 × 151 cm.

Fig. 5 Van Dyck, *The Balbi Children*. Infra-red photograph showing the sketched lines of the initial design.

Fig. 6 Van Dyck, *The Balbi Children*. X-ray detail of the oldest boy.

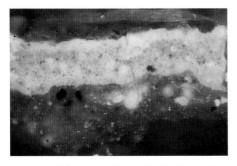

Plate 16 Van Dyck, *The Balbi Children*. Cross-section of mid-blue-green of the curtain with azurite scumbled over a pale blue consisting of indigo and white. A layer of orange-brown earth pigment is present beneath. The lowest layer is the brown ground. Original magnification 400×; actual magnification 240×.

Plate 17 Van Dyck, *The Balbi Children*. Deep blue-green of curtain with pure indigo glazed over a cochineal lake (carmine) and a small amount of natural azurite at the surface. Thin cross-section by transmitted light. Original magnification 250×; actual magnification 150×.

painting is also heavily discoloured, the overall tonality is probably, we must suppose, considerably more sombre than it was originally.

There are other effects involving discoloration that arise from pigment changes: the sky contains heavily discoloured smalt in oil, while the translucent dark brown foliage of the tree in the background consists largely of yellow-brown lake, black and degraded smalt. The oil medium here also appears to have darkened markedly. Where some green colour survives in the foliage, the paint contains verdigris, but a dark colour was evidently intended, since charcoal black is also present in the paint layer. The more obvious green of the sprig of foliage on the steps in the foreground preserves its colour as a result of the use of azurite mixed with yellow lake.[23]

It is evident from infra-red photography that Van Dyck drew the principal outlines of the figures, architecture and other smaller details directly on to the primed canvas, not all of which were followed precisely in the painting stage. There are two types of drawing visible: a dry black broken line, caught on the corrugations of the canvas weave, probably of charcoal or some kind of black chalk, and a more extensive use of fluid dark brown paint as a drawing medium, to reinforce the initial sketch. The dry black underdrawing can be seen most clearly just behind the painted outline of the oldest boy's cape and in the lower part of his costume, his cuffs and kneecap. Similar lines are present in the costumes and heads of the two other children (Fig. 5). The fluid brushed underdrawing in paint is visible in large areas of the composition around the figures and in the architecture, and particularly in areas where Van Dyck has not followed the underdrawn design in paint (Fig. 5). For example, the outline of the oldest boy's red cape was sketched in two different lower positions, not followed at the painting stage, and there are painted corrections to his knee and feet and to the legs and feet of the centre child. These lines are visible through the paint, but are more strongly revealed by infra-red examination, which also brings out the dark framework of the branches and trunk of the background tree, otherwise invisible on the picture. The infra-red image also shows minor details such as the bell attached to the leg of the left-hand chough, drawn but not painted, and a changed design for the hilt of the oldest boy's sword.

The composite X-ray photograph shows some changes made during the course of painting, as well as high radiographic contrast between the figures, particularly the heads of the children, the impasto

Plate 18 Van Dyck, *The Balbi Children*. Detail of the oldest boy's costume showing the application of impasto.

pun with the thin vermilion legs of the pair of choughs to which he gestures. Impasto highlights on the gold frogging and embroidery are painted in lead-tin yellow, while the cool, silvery greys of the lace, the ruff and the grey embroidery are a subtle combination of lead white with charcoal black and finely ground pale grey-blue smalt (Plate 18).

As a result of the depth of tone and glaze-like constitution of the dark costume worn by the boy at the centre, and the effect of darkened varnish, the intended colours here are now very difficult to read. Samples show very strongly coloured deep green glazes, based on verdigris in the doublet, which are modelled at the surface discontinuously with a dark red glaze to give a subtle *cangiante* effect to the velvet. The glazes also incorporate black pigment, rendering them profoundly dark. The application of red lake over a green glaze is a method Van Dyck may have borrowed from Venetian painting, in which it occurs widely, but is a technique not seen much elsewhere.[25]

Charity

Oak panel, 148 × 107.5 cm.

Painted in Antwerp in about 1627–8 after Van Dyck's return from Italy, *Charity* (Plate 19) is the only large-scale panel by the painter in the National Gallery Collection. The panel is a well-made oak construction comprising five vertical planks, butt-joined and glued with dowels (Fig. 7).[26] The ground layers are typical for an oak panel from Antwerp, and consist of a natural chalk lower layer bound in glue, with a very thin light greyish-brown *imprimatura*, probably oil-bound, on top. This *imprimatura* was applied evenly over the chalk ground and does not show the streaked appearance evident in many oil sketches and *modelli*

brushwork on their costumes and the background curtain, all of which absorb X-rays strongly, and the relatively radio-transparent background (Fig. 6). The most obvious pentimenti are around the heads of the oldest and youngest children, which were reduced a little in size, and in the lower part of the skirt of the youngest child.

Van Dyck's method of painting for the children's clothes and particularly for the large hanging curtain involves a more extensive glazing technique than is seen in his earlier work and, in fact, is not much used later. This presumably reflects an interest in Venetian methods of drapery painting for which glazes, particularly red lakes and 'copper resinate' types of green glaze, play such an important part. The background curtain to the right is a most elaborate piece of drapery painting and involves undercolours consisting of orange-toned pure vermilion modelled with vermilion, mixed with white and red earth, and then further modelled in two contrasting paints, one based on deep blue indigo and the other on a rich crimson red lake, likely to have been prepared from cochineal.[24] The final shimmering effect of the shot colours was achieved by glazing and scumbling with further red lake, red lake mixed with indigo, and pure indigo. In the lightest greenish-blue areas, there is a final scumble of mineral azurite (Plates 16 and 17).

Vermilion is also prominent in the sitters' clothes, where it is glazed with red lake in the youngest child's dress and used in a more solid form in the oldest boy's costume and in his stockings, which make a visual

Fig. 7 Van Dyck, *Charity*. Detail of the back of the thinned oak panel after removal of the cradle, showing original dowel at a join.

Plate 19 Anthony van Dyck, *Charity* (NG 6494), *c.*1627–8. Oak panel, 148 × 107.5 cm.

Fig. 8 Van Dyck, *Charity*. Infra-red photograph of the whole, showing initial sketched design in a dry drawing material and in fluid paint.

on panel, by Rubens, for example, and even on large fully worked-up paintings such as his *Samson and Delilah* (NG 6461).[27]

In designing *Charity*, Van Dyck seems to have used the underdrawing method noted above for the *Balbi Children*. There are traces in the infra-red photograph (Fig. 8) of a dry, dark drawing material around the main forms, particularly the babies' heads, hands and feet and also marking out the main fold lines in Charity's draperies. Working with the brush, these outlines were then re-inforced with a fluid warm dark red-brown paint, which can be seen on the surface of the picture, where the forms do not quite meet, as in, for example, the junctions of Charity's hand and her drapery, and defining the outlines of the babies' legs. This brushed underdrawing is more elaborate than the initial sketch, however, and infra-red examination indicates it to be an important and extensive stage in the genesis of the composition, fixing all the principal forms and their overlaps and allowing Van Dyck to leave reserves for each major element in the design. Because the ground and *imprimatura* do not exert an important effect on the

X-ray image of the painting, these reserves appear as particularly striking areas of contrast between X-ray dense areas, such as Charity's white drapery and the thinly painted arm of the right-hand child stretched across it, which registers as dark in the image (Fig. 9). Similarly, the heads of the two other babies are dark patches against drapery and sky paints. The strong modelling of the forms, where the paint layers contain substantial amounts of lead white, and the variety of brushwork types are also very clear from X-ray photographs (Fig. 10). Charity's white drapery is painted in long fluid strokes of some thickness, whereas the flesh tones are executed very smoothly, first by a stippling action, evident in the X-ray, then brushed out and blended from the lights to the shadows, effacing virtually all texture. This kind of effect is only really achievable on panel and must have been a reason for the choice of a wood support rather than canvas in order to produce a rather enamel-like finish to the flesh painting.[28] A panel had perhaps been specified in the commission.

The X-ray photograph also shows how little modification was made to the design during the

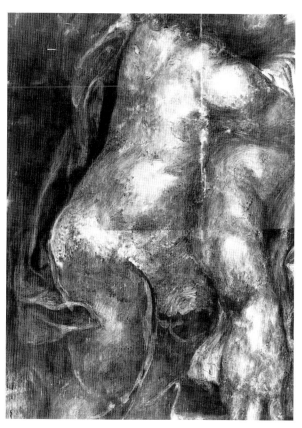

Fig. 9 Van Dyck, *Charity*. Composite X-ray photograph showing the variety of brushwork in the painting and the use of reserves for forms.

Fig. 10 Van Dyck, *Charity*. X-ray detail of the body of the child at the left, showing the brushwork in the build-up of the flesh tones.

course of painting. The only pentimento of any significance involves the blue drapery around Charity's neck, which also floats behind her. Initially, it appears, this was to be a smaller area of blue, with a patch of white drapery occupying the position just around and behind the left-hand child's head. This was then painted over with ultramarine and connected to the blue around Charity's neck by glazing ultramarine over her shoulder to make a continuous and larger area of blue. Some undecipherable change to the background appears to have been made beneath the wide dark strip in the background to the left, but this registers only in the infra-red photograph.

Van Dyck's *Charity* is generally seen as a strongly Venetian-influenced work with Titian-like colouring. While this is clearly so for the design, and in the powerful combination of relatively unbroken colours of the blue, red and white draperies, there is evidence that Van Dyck intended a rather more muted effect. This interpretation rests on the observation that colour has changed in the picture and on the detection of unstable pigments. The sky paint, for example,

Plate 20 Van Dyck, *Charity*. Detail of Charity's ultramarine-containing drapery.

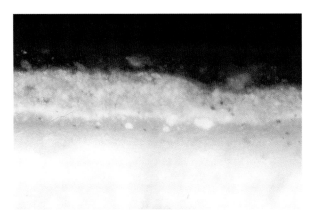

Plate 21 Van Dyck, *Charity*. Cross-section of Charity's brownish-red drapery, lower left edge. There is an underpaint of vermilion, earth pigments and white and over this an orange-red glaze containing red and yellow lake pigments. The chalk ground and a very thin greyish-brown *imprimatura* are visible beneath. Original magnification 400×; actual magnification 320×.

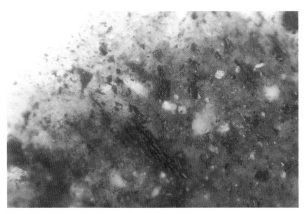

Plate 22 Van Dyck, *Charity*. Olive-brown of the curtain, upper right. Top surface of a paint sample containing yellow lake pigment, some yellow ochre and charcoal black. Original magnification 275×; actual magnification 220×.

consists of smalt with white, which has discoloured to some degree; however, a stormy sky with areas of grey was intended, since some parts consist just of grey paint, and where there is smalt it is underpainted with a layer of grey. Since brilliant blue natural ultramarine is used elsewhere in the picture – in Charity's fluttering blue drapery – a powerfully Italianate blue sky was clearly not Van Dyck's choice. Similarly, although the rich, pure bright colour of ultramarine in a drapery is Venetian in conception, in Charity's drapery here it is underpainted with a very strongly coloured deep blue-green layer of indigo, which shifts the colour to a rather more greenish and dark tone than ultramarine otherwise would exhibit (Plate 20). In fact, in the shadows of the blue drapery at the left and in the swathe at Charity's neck, only indigo is present.

There are other signs of Van Dyck's intention to diminish the strength of the pure bright colours that his choice of palette for this picture would have permitted and this is particularly the case in the large area of red-brown drapery that occupies the lower third of the picture. This drapery is constructed from several pigments combined in a variety of ways in order to produce a range of colour, light and shade. It is apparent also that there has been some colour change, presumably as a result of the action of light, since a strip of drapery about two cm wide at the left edge is a rather brighter, more cherry-red colour than the paint it adjoins, and must have been protected from light by an earlier frame or moulding. The paint here consists of a mixture of red and yellow lake pigments (Plate 21). The red component has been

identified as a lake produced from a cochineal dyestuff, while the translucent yellow is presumably a plant dyestuff-based lake.[29] Both would be vulnerable to the action of light, and would tend to produce a colour shift towards a browner or more orange tone in the initial phases of fading. In the brownest areas of the drapery, there are mixtures of yellow lake with charcoal black, giving the paint a very dark olive undertone, and there are also areas glazed in Cassel earth, which in oil medium functions as a warm brown glaze. The lightest, pinkish-brown tones are thinner glazes of red and yellow lakes over a pale pink preliminary layer of lead white tinted with a little vermilion, laid in at the first stage of the drapery painting to represent just the highlight areas; the X-ray image shows this stage of underpainting clearly.

The method of construction of this drapery is therefore rather complex, but subtle transitions of colour are involved, and since the extent of colour change cannot be known, Van Dyck's precise intentions are difficult to judge: it is certain, though, that a straightforward Venetian type of deep red drapery, based on purple-red-toned glazes, was not his aim. Although altered by colour change in some of the pigments, a more subtle, less vivid colour effect would have resulted from the method of painting employed. In the background curtain, to the right, and in the very dark panel behind the figure of Charity to the left, dark glazes similar to those used for the deepest shadows of the drapery are present: charcoal black with yellow lake for the former and Cassel earth in the latter, and these features also serve to lower the overall key of the painting (Plate 22).

Plate 23 Anthony van Dyck, *Carlo and Ubaldo see Rinaldo conquered by Love for Armida* (NG 877.2), 1634–5. Oak panel, 57 × 41.5 cm.

Carlo and Ubaldo see Rinaldo conquered by Love for Armida

Oak panel, 57 × 41.5 cm.

Painted in *grisaille* on an oak panel, and squared for transposition of the design to an engraving plate. The composition was engraved as a direct copy, that is, not in reverse, by Pieter de Jode the Younger in 1644; Van Dyck's composition is earlier and thought to date from 1634–5 (Plate 23). The panel for this *modello* is made up of two vertical oak planks, one slightly wider than the other (average 26.3 cm wide, and average 15.1 cm wide), bearing a clear Antwerp panel-maker's mark of a castle and the palms of two hands on the wider plank (Fig.11) and the initials 'MV', probably for Michiel Vriendt, cut into the back of the narrower member. This Antwerp mark was in use between 1619 and 1638.[30] Under the semi-monochrome paint layers, there is a pure white chalk ground, and an exceedingly thin greyish *imprimatura*. It is not known whether it was common for the *imprimatura* for panel paintings, and perhaps the chalk ground also, to be applied by the painter's workshop rather than by the panel-maker, although it seems likely that fully grounded and primed panels were also available from stock in the Low Countries and certainly in the Netherlands.[31] The ground structure and *imprimatura* are very similar to those on Van Dyck's *Charity*, described above.

The first stage of execution by Van Dyck was a very fine brushed underdrawing in dark greyish-brown and translucent deep brown paints, applied directly over the *imprimatura*. This follows Van Dyck's usual practice, although on a more delicate scale, of drawing in more than one colour of fluid paint; this can be seen, for example, in the raised arm of the putto to the left, the upper profile of which is drawn in a greyish-brown tone, whereas the lower edge of the arm is marked by a thin line of semi-transparent dark brown. Examination of the painting under the stereomicroscope has shown that the next stage was the application of a few crucial details at the centre of the composition in drawn lines and small patches of a rich red-brown paint, not used anywhere else in the composition.[32] The largest area of this kind is the warm deep shadow around the left side of Armida's face and over her left breast, and the smaller area of shadow under her right eye (Plate 24). A similar paint can be seen in the left eye and around the face of the putto leaning on Rinaldo's arm as well as in the head and body of the putto at the left edge of the composition (Plate 25).

After this, Van Dyck worked up the composition

Fig. 11 Van Dyck, *Carlo and Ubaldo see Rinaldo conquered by Love for Armida*. Detail of the reverse of the panel, showing the panel-maker's brand for the City of Antwerp.

using modelling and further more linear brushwork, first in thin warm brown tones, followed by areas of thin greyish modelling. The last stages would have been the application of white and greyish-white highlights in lead white and lead white combined with a little black pigment. The initially applied browner shadows are largely Cassel earth, with some black pigment and a small proportion of finely ground, pale-coloured azurite, likely to have been added to assist the paint to dry (Plate 27). The grey wash-like tones of the early stage of the painting consist of finely ground wood charcoal mixed with lead white and chalk.

Close examination of the way in which the grid of incised lines cuts through the paint indicates, strongly, that the squaring up must have been carried out by Van Dyck or by a studio assistant and not as late as the engraving derived from it. The incisions pass through most of the paint layers, but they do not divide the final, thickest, small highlight touches of pure lead white, applied at the very last stage of painting, for example those on Armida's nose, the top of Rinaldo's boots, the small glass decanters in the foreground, and elsewhere (Plate 26). There is no doubt that these highlights are original. Clearly, Van Dyck's aim was a composition designed from the outset as a source for an engraved print.

Plate 24 Van Dyck, *Carlo and Ubaldo see Rinaldo conquered by Love for Armida*. Detail of Armida's head, showing the warm red-brown shadows of the early stage in the design and the subsequent application of browns, greys and whites.

Plate 25 Van Dyck, *Carlo and Ubaldo see Rinaldo conquered by Love for Armida*. Detail of the putto leaning on Rinaldo's arm. Red-brown paint marks out the left-hand side of the head and the left eye.

Plate 26 Van Dyck, *Carlo and Ubaldo see Rinaldo conquered by Love for Armida*. Detail of the decanters, foreground, lower edge, right. The final white impasto highlights are not bisected by the incised lines of the grid.

Plate 27 Van Dyck, *Carlo and Ubaldo see Rinaldo conquered by Love for Armida*. Paint sample from brownish glaze for foliage, upper right, containing Cassel earth, charcoal black and a little white pigment. There is also some finely ground azurite present. Top surface. Original magnification 240×; actual magnification 200×.

Plate 28 Anthony van Dyck, *The Abbé Scaglia adoring the Virgin and Child* (NG 4889), 1634–5. Canvas, 107 × 120 cm.

The Abbé Scaglia adoring the Virgin and Child

Canvas, plain weave (tabby): 14↕ x 13↔ threads/cm;
107 × 120 cm.

Painted in Brussels about 1634–5 (Plate 28), the donor has been identified as the Abbé Scaglia from an engraved portrait in *The Iconography* and from the documented full-length portrait of the same sitter, currently on loan to the National Gallery (*The Abbé Scaglia*, probably 1635; Fig. 12). There is also a drawing by Van Dyck of the donor's head in the British Museum. The composition showing the Abbé Scaglia with the Virgin and Child derives from a lost painting by Titian and a pen and ink sketch of the design occurs in Van Dyck's Italian sketchbook held in the British Museum (Fig. 13).

The oval field of the National Gallery picture occupies the whole of the rectangular landscape-format canvas, the periphery of which was evidently marked out in fluid brownish-black paint as the first stage of the design. Traces of the drawn oval can be seen when the picture is removed from its frame and the surrounding unpainted light greyish-brown ground is also exposed. The ground consists of a

Fig. 12 (left) Anthony van Dyck, *The Abbé Scaglia*, *c.*1635. Private Collection. Detail of the head.

Fig. 13 (above) Anthony van Dyck, drawing after Titian, in his Italian sketchbook. London, British Museum.

Fig. 14 (below) Van Dyck, *The Abbé Scaglia adoring the Virgin and Child*. Infra-red photograph.

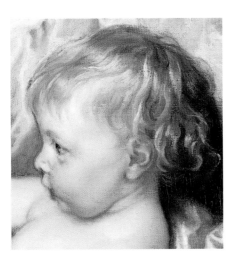

Plate 29 Van Dyck, *The Abbé Scaglia adoring the Virgin and Child*. Detail of the Child's profile.

Plate 32 Anthony van Dyck, *The Princesses Elizabeth and Anne*, Edinburgh, National Portrait Gallery, *c*.1635–40. Detail. Oil on canvas, 29.8 × 41.8 cm.

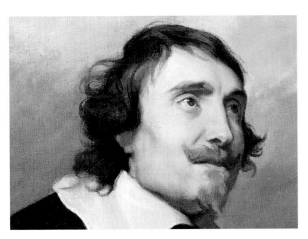

Plate 30 Van Dyck, *The Abbé Scaglia adoring the Virgin and Child*. Detail of Abbé Scaglia's head.

Plate 31 Van Dyck, *The Abbé Scaglia adoring the Virgin and Child*. Detail of the Virgin's pink drapery.

single coherent layer of lead white combined with some charcoal black, Cassel earth and a little yellow earth. This simple priming structure, the main components of which are lead white in oil, is probably partly responsible for the very well-preserved state of the picture. A similar ground occurs in Van Dyck's large-format family group portrait, *Count John Nassau-Siegen and his Family* (Sussex, Firle Estate), painted in Brussels in 1634, but there it forms the upper ground of a two-layered system.[33]

Further drawing of the design in dark paint, which follows Van Dyck's habitual manner of working, is evident from an infra-red photograph, and is particularly visible in the Virgin's draperies, her face and hands and those of the donor (Fig. 14). Drawing in paint, involving warmer colours, occurs in the figure of the Child, around the chest and arms and in the definition of the profile of the face (Plate 29). Infra-red light also reveals two important pentimenti. A dark strip of shadow under part of the blue drapery at the Virgin's right knee, running to the lower edge of the composition, indicates that initially Scaglia's black sleeve and robe were broader and further to the right. In the final design Van Dyck also raised the Child's foot by about two cm and the infra-red image shows a patch of shadow placed to define the first position of the sole of the foot, using a technique seen also in the oil sketch on canvas of the *Princesses Elizabeth and Anne* (Plate 32) where the back of Princess Elizabeth's head is marked by a halo of thin dark paint. (See also *Lord John Stuart and his Brother, Lord Bernard Stuart*, pp. 80–1.)

The pure blue sky of *The Abbé Scaglia adoring the Virgin and Child* is painted using high-quality lapis lazuli ultramarine, mixed with white. The greyish-mauve parts of the sky, seen around the donor's shoulders, consist of charcoal black with white and some red lake and red earth pigment (Plate 30).

The method of painting as a whole is assured and straightforward; it is only in the execution of the Virgin's draperies that any complexity occurs. In both the blue and red of the Virgin's dress, three or four separate tones and constitutions of paint are used to achieve the final results. The shadows of the blue fabric covering the Virgin's knees were blocked in first using a dark shade of indigo mixed with white, followed by a lighter tone of a similar composition to indicate the mid-tones. The final layers consist of glazes of natural ultramarine, varying in thickness according to the modelling beneath. The upper part of the dress relies on the range of colour qualities of three differently toned reds: vermilion, red lake and a strongly coloured brownish-red earth; these are combined with white pigment and charcoal black in certain areas. Modelling of the mid-tones was carried out first in a pure pink tint of vermilion mixed with white, followed by the shadow values in a paint of unmixed red-brown earth. The upper layers consist of pink paints comprising red lake and white, red lake glazes, with charcoal black added to the lake in the darkest, most saturated shadows of the folds, particularly to the right of the dress in the sleeve (Plate 31). Some fading of the red lakes at the surface has allowed the colour of the brownish underlayer containing earth pigment to become more prominent.

Plate 33 Van Dyck, *The Abbé Scaglia adoring the Virgin and Child*. Cross-section of deep green curtain with a lead-tin yellow and azurite underpaint and a glaze containing indigo and black. The single beige ground is visible beneath. Original magnification 735×; actual magnification 440×.

The combination of colours in the draperies, with blues based on indigo and ultramarine and the red and pink dress influenced by the use of lake glazes, as well as the cool white and subtle grey of the cloth in which the Child is wrapped, strongly echoes the colour composition of *Charity*, which also has a dull greenish curtain in the background to the right, although in the present picture the colour key as a whole is rather higher.

The background curtain in *The Abbé Scaglia adoring the Virgin and Child* is painted as a scumble of indigo and a little white, or a glaze of very intense indigo where the curtain is in deep shadow, over a solid mid-green underlayer consisting of azurite mixed with lead-tin yellow (Plate 33). To the right, where the curtain possesses a dark greenish-brown tone, the surface glaze of indigo passes over a mid-brown underlayer of black and white with red and brown earth pigments.

Lady Elizabeth Thimbelby and Dorothy, Viscountess Andover

Canvas, plain weave (tabby): 11↕ × 11↔ threads/cm; 132 × 149 cm.

Painted in England around 1637, this represents two sisters, Elizabeth at the left, and Dorothy at the right, daughters of Thomas, Viscount Savage (Plate 34). The painting was probably commissioned to mark Dorothy's marriage in 1637 to Charles Howard, Viscount Andover, and this accounts for the winged putto with a basket of roses, attribute of Saint Dorothy, patron saint of brides and newly-weds.

The canvas is a single piece of fairly coarse linen and the format is similar to several of Van Dyck's double portraits from this period, notably *Thomas Killigrew and William, Lord Crofts* (signed and dated 1638, canvas, 133 × 144 cm; Windsor Castle, Royal Collection) and *Thomas Wentworth, 1st Earl of Strafford with Sir Philip Mainwaring* (1640, canvas, 123 × 140 cm; Wentworth Woodhouse, Earl Fitzwilliam).[34] For *Lady Thimbelby and Viscountess Andover*, the ground is a double-layered system with a lower layer of a strong red-brown comprising mainly red iron oxide combined with calcium carbonate, over which a mid grey-brown priming was applied, consisting of lead white, charcoal black and some red and brown earth pigment (see Plate 37).[35] This upper ground colour can be glimpsed in a few places through the overlying paint layers, for example at the junction of the basket and Lady Elizabeth's white dress, although in this composition the ground is in the main fully concealed by paint.

Plate 34 Anthony van Dyck, *Lady Elizabeth Thimbelby and Dorothy, Viscountess Andover* (NG 6437), *c.*1637. Canvas, 132 × 149 cm.

Fig. 15 Van Dyck, *Lady Elizabeth Thimbelby and Dorothy, Viscountess Andover*. Detail of Viscountess Dorothy's head.

Fig. 16 Van Dyck, *Lady Elizabeth Thimbelby and Dorothy, Viscountess Andover*. X-ray detail of Viscountess Dorothy's head.

As in many of Van Dyck's paintings, the first stage of execution was an outline sketch in brushwork to fix the essentials of the composition. This was carried out in a thin warm brown paint, and traces can be seen at the surface outlining the lower edge of Viscountess Dorothy's arm and particularly in the profile of the winged putto. The infra-red photograph reveals little more of this underdrawing than can be seen with the naked eye. Paint cross-sections show a certain amount of underpainting in a few passages, but this is not so extensive as to merit the description of the underlayers as a 'dead coloured' stage. Underpaint layers are apparent in, for example, the yellow dress, the basket of flowers and the background curtain.

Much of the painting was composed *alla prima* in the most direct manner and this emerges also from the X-ray image, which shows the heads of the sitters boldly and simply worked within the outlines of the brushed underdrawing (Figs. 15 and 16). Very few pentimenti are present, only the suggestion of a suppressed background column behind and just to the left of Viscountess Dorothy's head, which is visible also in an infra-red photograph, and some minor adjustment around the tops of the sitters' heads and

to their hairstyles, although even as detailed a feature as the ringlets on Viscountess Dorothy's forehead was left in reserve, having been allowed for in the planning, since these are not painted over the flesh tone.

The palette for *Lady Thimbelby and Viscountess Andover* is fairly standard for the period, and the following have been identified in samples: smalt, azurite, ultramarine (in minor quantities), green verditer,[36] vermilion, red and yellow lakes, lead-tin yellow, a variety of earth pigments including Cassel earth, black pigments and white. These pigments are used singly and in mixture to form the paint layers; the binding medium has been identified as linseed oil throughout the picture (see the section on Van Dyck's medium, pp. 84–6).

The bluer parts of the sky are painted in smalt of a grey-blue tone, and blended into darker greys in which black pigment, mixed with some smalt, predominates, while the strongest blue patch at the horizon, near Lady Elizabeth's forearm, contains smalt and white mixed with red lake to produce a greyish-mauve tone. The very dark green background curtain, against the sky, has a glaze-like quality for the fabric. It is painted in a mixture of green verditer

Plate 35 Van Dyck, *Lady Elizabeth Thimbelby and Dorothy, Viscountess Andover*. Thin cross-section of the green background curtain. The paint consists largely of artificial malachite (green verditer) and yellow lake pigment. Transmitted light. Original magnification 700×; actual magnification 420×.

Plate 38 Van Dyck, *Lady Elizabeth Thimbelby and Dorothy, Viscountess Andover*. Paint sample from the flesh of Lady Elizabeth's hand containing lead white, red earth, vermilion, Cassel earth, golden ochre, charcoal black and a small quantity of natural ultramarine. Top surface. Original magnification 275×; actual magnification 165×.

Plate 36 Van Dyck, *Lady Elizabeth Thimbelby and Dorothy, Viscountess Andover*. Detail of the winged putto's drapery.

Plate 37 Van Dyck, *Lady Elizabeth Thimbelby and Dorothy, Viscountess Andover*. Cross-section of the orange paint of Viscountess Dorothy's satin sleeve comprising several layers of strongly coloured yellow earth pigment, vermilion, white and black. The lowermost two layers of orange-brown and grey represent the double ground. Original magnification 400×; actual magnification 240×.

(artificial malachite) and yellow lake, with, in the shadows, the same combination of pigments and the addition of a great deal of charcoal black (Plate 35). The stronger, more opaque greens of the rose leaves in the basket held by the putto, on the other hand, consist of lead-tin yellow, yellow lake and azurite.

The winged putto's pinkish-red drapery is based on vermilion with white, glazed in the shadows with red lake (Plate 36), and the much darker red-brown tones of Viscountess Dorothy's silk shawl are produced by combinations of finely ground vermilion, red earth and black pigment, mixed, but not glazed, with red lake. Lead-tin yellow ('type I')[37] is responsible for the bright yellow, highest impasto parts of the Viscountess's golden satin dress and also for the embroidery on Lady Elizabeth's fawn-coloured shawl. The darker, more golden, tones of the dress consist of a deep yellow ochre with white and a little crystalline red earth (haematite), while the more orange colours of the sleeve contain a higher proportion of haematite, as well as lead-tin yellow, yellow ochre and red lake (see Plate 37). The plain whites of Lady Elizabeth's dress are just pure white, painted over an understructure made up of cool and warmer greys, the cool tones containing wood charcoal while the warmer brownish greys incorporate Cassel earth.

Van Dyck's simple but highly accomplished working of the flesh tones makes use of virtually pure lead white with very small quantities of finely ground red earth, vermilion and Cassel earth in the lights, grading to tones which are just a shade darker and creamier by the addition of a little translucent golden ochre and small quantities of black pigment. For the distinctly cool shadows, for example of Lady Elizabeth's raised hand, Van Dyck has added just a trace of lapis lazuli ultramarine (Plate 38).

Equestrian Portrait of Charles I

Canvas, herringbone-weave ticking; 367 × 292 cm.

This is one of two equestrian portraits of Charles I by Van Dyck and thought to date from 1637–8 (Plate 39); the composition and its relationship to a smaller version in the Royal Collection, once thought to be a *modello* for the National Gallery picture, are discussed by Gregory Martin, who suggested that the picture at Windsor is based on NG 1172 and is not a preliminary work.[38] The second composition, also in the Royal Collection, painted slightly earlier in 1633, *Charles I with M. de St Antoine*, is roughly the same size as the National Gallery picture, measuring 368 × 270 cm. There is a drawing in the British Museum which might be related to the present composition.

The canvas support for this life-size equestrian portrait is made up of two roughly equal-size pieces of thick, heavy canvas ticking with a tight herringbone-weave and a striped pattern, apparently in black (Fig. 17).[39] The warp threads run horizontally and the adjacent edges of the two sections of canvas roughly bisect the centre of the composition, in a line just below the horse's bit, the armour covering King Charles's thigh and through the neck of the equerry holding the helmet at the right side. The canvas pieces are now held in place by a lining canvas, with chalk putty filling the join between the two sections, but there is evidence that originally the two were sewn together and there is still some stitching to be seen at the right side in an X-ray photograph. It seems likely that the herringbone-weave canvas was preferred because of its particular strength and low tendency to sag or distort when used for such a large composition; it is significant that a similar canvas made of ticking was used for the even larger *Pembroke Family Group* at Wilton House.[40] The back of the original canvas of the National Gallery painting carries the stamp of Charles I's collection (Fig. 18).

The canvas bears a double ground: a thin red-brown lower layer, principally reddish ochre and calcium carbonate,[41] with a second oil-based priming of a light, slightly brownish grey. This second ground is composed of lead white with charcoal black and some brownish ochre or Cassel earth (Plate 40). The thinness of the lower ground appears to be connected with the tight patterned weave of the canvas, and it only just fills the interstices of the grain. The upper light-coloured ground is thicker; it seems probable that the primed canvas was made up specially in Van Dyck's studio for this commission from the royal household.

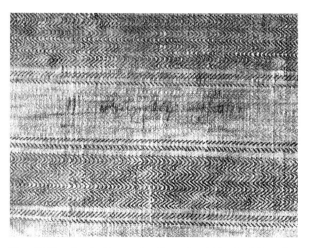

Fig. 17 Van Dyck, *Equestrian Portrait of Charles I*. Detail of the original canvas (herringbone ticking).

Fig. 18 Van Dyck, *Equestrian Portrait of Charles I*. Detail of Charles I's collection mark on reverse of original canvas.

A single sample of sky paint and ground was taken at the time of the cleaning of the painting in 1952. For the purposes of the present technical description, a few further samples were taken to establish the materials used, but they do not provide a complete survey of the artist's technique. As in other of his compositions, Van Dyck's preliminary drawing on the ground is sketched then worked up in fairly broad brushwork using a dark brown translucent paint. This is now difficult to make out on the picture, since the surface is dark, and the varnish discoloured and also a little blanched. However, outlines of forms can be seen where the paint is sketchy and cursorily applied, as in the canopy of branches overhanging the King's head and in the foreground, particularly around the horse's hooves and legs. Initial planning of the design was clearly quite thorough, since reserves are left for details as minor as the grey-green leaves of the wilting thistle in the lower left corner.

Plate 39 Anthony van Dyck, *Equestrian Portrait of Charles I* (NG 1172), *c*.1637–8. Canvas, 367 × 292 cm.

An infra-red photograph brings out the dark painted lines of the first stages of sketching rather more clearly, and reveals, particularly, changes to Charles's *culet* – the armour protecting his hips – which was first painted lower and much narrower, and also shows modifications to the rear part of the saddle and saddle cloth (Fig. 19). Gregory Martin suggested that the skirt of the rear part of the armour – the *culet* – in its present position, was a later addition, probably not by Van Dyck;[42] it can be seen in the infra-red photograph to pass over the sky and part of the background foliage behind the sitter and is painted rather differently from the rest of the armour.

The dominant tonality of the picture is muted and low in key; this is partly intentional, but there are also changes in the materials of the painting which must have increased the effect. The sky paint consists of greyish-blue smalt mixed with white, with a thin discontinuous layer of natural ultramarine and white painted on top in the bluest areas (Plate 40); nevertheless the colour overall is rather sombre. Martin believed that the upper layer of sky paint was badly damaged,[43] but this seems not to be the case, although there is some blanching in the ultramarine-containing paint, and, in addition, the smalt has probably partially discoloured. The slightly greyish blues of the saddle cloth consist of indigo mixed with white; cross-sections show the blue pigment has faded quite badly. The brownish reds of this cloth are made up of red lake pigment mixed with vermilion containing particularly fine needle-shaped particles. Some loss of colour of the lake seems likely, since where it is protected from light under overlying paint layers the colour is richer and stronger. The reds and brownish reds of the equerry's sleeve employ similar mixtures of red lake and vermilion over a red-brown underpaint of red earth pigment, black and white.

The dark glazes used for foreground, foliage and middle distance consist of mixtures of a variety of types of ochre, Cassel earth and black, with yellow lake, while the stronger colours of greenish foliage contain mineral azurite, ochre, yellow lake and black, in various proportions according to the colour and opacity of the paint. The more translucent greens contain a higher proportion of azurite and lake; those which are more solid incorporate white pigment and ochre. In spite of the darkened varnish on the picture, the reflections painted as white highlights on the King's armour and the touches of gold in lead-tin yellow on the stirrup still catch the light as Van Dyck intended.

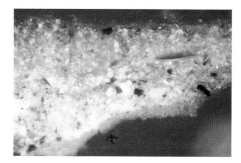

Plate 40 Van Dyck, *Equestrian Portrait of Charles I*. Cross-section from the brightest blue of the sky, upper left, containing lapis lazuli ultramarine and smalt, with an underlayer containing smalt. The double ground of red-brown followed by warm grey can be seen beneath. Original magnification 200×; actual magnification 120×.

Fig. 19 Van Dyck, *Equestrian Portrait of Charles I*. Infra-red photograph detail, showing modifications to the figure of the King.

Lord John Stuart and his Brother, Lord Bernard Stuart

Canvas: 10↕ × 12↔ threads/cm;[44] 237.5 × 146 cm.

This late, life-size double portrait (Plate 41) shows the two youngest sons of the 3rd Duke of Lennox, Lord John Stuart on the left, and Lord Bernard Stuart slightly in front at the right; it is thought to date from 1638 or early in 1639 when the Stuart brothers left England to tour the Continent for three years. The technique is characteristic of certain of Van Dyck's late portraits in which all painterly attention is devoted to the figures of the sitters and their draperies and little to the background and setting, which are left in a cursory sketchy state. *The Portrait of Sir Thomas Chaloner*, c.1637, in Leningrad (The State Hermitage Museum) and *Olivia Porter, Wife of Endymion Porter*, also c.1637 (Private Collection), represent similar cases from this period.[45]

The National Gallery double portrait is painted on a medium-weight plain-weave canvas with a single layer of light biscuit-coloured ground made of lead white mixed with a fairly small quantity of translucent brown earth, probably Cassel earth. Preliminary drawing in thin dark paint of the figures and the designs of their draperies is extensive and unusually detailed; it can be seen on the surface of the picture and more clearly in an infra-red photograph. It is perhaps most obvious along the outlines and edges of Lord Bernard's blue and silver cloak, around his chin, gloved hand and calfskin boots (Fig. 20). Similar underdrawing is used for the figure of Lord John, but it is broader and freer in style. The infra-red photograph also shows a very dark oval patch framing Lord Bernard's head, made up of a layer of charcoal black pigment beneath the thin wash-like brown background, and this was evidently used to frame and place the head before it was painted (Fig. 20). It is part of the first compositional phase involving the underdrawing. Van Dyck used a similar device early in the painting to frame the head in the full-length *Portrait of the Abbé Scaglia* of about 1635, currently on loan to the National Gallery (Private Collection). The head of Lord John Stuart lacks this dark surround, but the curls and waves of the hair of both young men are evident in the underdrawn stage of the heads left in reserve in the background (Fig. 21).

The greys and browns of the architectural background setting are painted extremely thinly and sketchily in single layers of white with varying proportions of semi-translucent earth pigments and black. The loose and evidently rapid fluid brushwork can easily be made out on the picture surface,

Plate 41 Anthony van Dyck, *Lord John Stuart and his Brother, Lord Bernard Stuart* (NG 6518), 1638–9. Canvas, 237.5 × 146 cm.

particularly in the plinth and steps to the left, where the ground can be seen through the thin surface paint.

The draperies are constructed in a more elaborate and highly finished manner. The sections of blue satin of Lord Bernard's clothes are undermodelled with indigo in the shadows and indigo combined with white for the mid-tones (Plate 42).[46] The surface was then scumbled with greenish mineral azurite and azurite mixed with indigo using a technique that follows the painting of the background curtain in the earlier *Balbi Children*. The final effect in the use of these materials lends a particular richness and sheen to the painting of the fabric. Lord John Stuart's brown and gold costume (Plate 43) is a similarly accomplished piece of painting and employs a technique close to that used for Viscountess Dorothy's yellow and gold dress in the double portrait of *Lady Thimbelby and Dorothy, Viscountess Andover* painted about a year earlier. In Lord John's drapery the brightest, lightest yellow highlights are pure lead-

Fig. 20 Van Dyck, *Lord John Stuart and his Brother, Lord Bernard Stuart*. Infra-red photograph detail showing initial dark sketching lines and lay-in.

Plate 42 Van Dyck, *Lord John Stuart and his Brother, Lord Bernard Stuart*. Cross-section of the dark blue satin of Lord Bernard's cloak with azurite and indigo at the surface over a layer of indigo and white. The light biscuit-coloured ground is visible beneath. Original magnification 700×; actual magnification 420×.

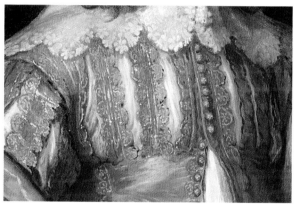

Plate 43 Van Dyck, *Lord John Stuart and his Brother, Lord Bernard Stuart*. Detail of Lord John's brown and gold costume.

Fig. 21 Van Dyck, *Lord John Stuart and his Brother, Lord Bernard Stuart*. Detail of Lord Bernard's head.

tin yellow, which grade into darker more golden-brown colours incorporating yellow ochre, lead white and some crystalline red earth pigment (haematite). The deeper, brownish glaze-like shadows consist largely of a reddish ochre with Cassel earth and some yellow ochre. Analytical examination of the organic components of the glaze-like darker yellows showed the incorporation of a bistre or pitch-like material, derived from pyrolysed birch tree bark (*Betula alba*).[47] The medium in these passages has been identified as walnut oil (see also p. 86).

Van Dyck evidently used this dark translucent bistre fairly widely in the darks of the picture, since it occurs also in the dark brown background behind Lord John Stuart, as well as in a dark shadow of the grey and silver lining of Lord Bernard Stuart's cloak; in both these areas the medium is linseed rather than walnut oil.

Notes and references

1. Relatively few pictures in Italy are on panel at this date and also rather few in England. In Flanders, however, large-scale panel supports of oak were still common at the beginning of the seventeenth century, for example Rubens's great altarpiece, *The Descent from the Cross*, painted 1611–14 for Antwerp Cathedral, the central panel of which measures 4.21 × 3.11 m. Each wing measures 4.21 m x 1.53 m. See A. Philippot and P. Philippot, 'La descente de croix de Rubens: technique picturale et traitement', *Bulletin de L'Institut Royal du Patrimoine Artistique*, VI, 1963, pp. 8–9.

2. Painting on copper panel supports allows even more refined and detailed brushwork and a very high degree of finish. See M.K. Kommanecky, I. Horovitz and N. Eastaugh, 'Antwerp Artists and the Practice of Painting on Copper', *Painting Techniques: History, Materials and Studio Practice'*, Preprints of the IIC Dublin Congress, 7–11 September 1998, ed. by A. Roy and P. Smith, London 1998, p. 139.

3. See C. Christensen, M. Palmer and M. Swicklik, 'Van Dyck's Painting Technique, His Writings, and Three Paintings in the National Gallery of Art' in *Anthony van Dyck*, exh. cat., National Gallery of Art, Washington, ed. by A.K. Wheelock, S.J. Barnes and J.S. Held, Washington DC, 1990, pp. 45–52.

4. Paint samples from the National Gallery Van Dycks were examined by standard methods in use in the Scientific Department of the National Gallery, particularly optical and scanning electron microscopy (with EDX analysis of cross-sections), X-ray diffraction analysis, gas-chromatography linked to mass-spectrometry, Fourier-transform infra-red micro-spectrophotometry (FTIR) and high-performance liquid chromatography (HPLC).

5. G. Martin, *National Gallery Catalogues, The Flemish School, 1600–1900*, London 1970, pp. 26–67.

6. The canvas thread counts are averages taken from X-ray images of the paintings. The vertical double arrow represents the thread count in the vertical direction and vice versa.

7. See Christensen, Palmer and Swicklik, cited in note 3, pp. 47–9.

8. M.W. Ainsworth et al., *Art and Autoradiography: Insights Into the Genesis of Paintings by Rembrandt, Van Dyck and Vermeer*, The Metropolitan Museum of Art, New York 1982, pp. 12–18.

9. Ainsworth et al., cited in note 8, p. 18.

10. Lead-tin yellow shown to be 'type I' by XRD. See JCPDS File No. 11–233.

11. Wheelock, Barnes and Held, cited in note 3, cat. 21, pp. 135–7.

12. Charcoal black (small cole) was known to be a cool, bluish black. '..note that Small cole or Charcole is a blew blacke, & Sea cole makes a Red Blacke...' in BL MS Harley 6376, f.92. This optical property was exploited in the mixtures to create purple colours when combined with white and red lake, or, for duller colours, in combination with red earth.

13. See J. Plesters, '"Samson and Delilah": Rubens and the Art and Craft of Painting on Panel', *National Gallery Technical Bulletin*, 7, 1983, p. 45 and Plates 5g–l, pp. 48–9.

14. Martin, cited in note 5, pp. 58–61. Martin describes the picture as 'After (?) van Dyck'.

15. Wheelock, Barnes and Held, cited in note 3, cat. 30, pp. 158–61.

16. Calcium carbonate confirmed in the upper ground by EDX.

17. This new grey ground is fairly thick and highly heterogenous; moreover, the constitution varies from place to place. Although dominantly a grey colour consisting principally of lead white with a carbon black pigment (not charcoal), also present in varying quantities are azurite, red lead, red lake and a number of different earth pigment types. It is possible, therefore, that this layer is composed of 'palette scrapings', that is, recycled paint from the palette or *pencelier*. Material of this kind is strongly drying on account of the partially polymerised oil present, as well as the drying influence of certain pigments. See also note 18 below.

18. In addition to the lead-white content which exerts a siccative action on the oil medium, azurite and red lead are also strongly drying pigments.

19. *Saint Martin dividing his Cloak* (overall 258 × 243 cm) in the Royal Collection has an original canvas strip addition at the right-hand side, about 38 cm in width. This modification seems to relate to major changes that Van Dyck made to the composition during execution particularly in the background architecture and figure group to the right. See Oliver Millar, *The Tudor, Stuart and Early Georgian Pictures in the Collection of Her Majesty the Queen*, Text Volume, London, 1963, p. 104. Cross-sections taken by Aviva Burnstock in 1990 on either side of the seam joining the added strip to the main canvas showed that this was grounded after the strip was attached, and that the priming passes over the ground layers on the main canvas. Unpublished report in the Scientific Department.

20. Wheelock, Barnes and Held, cited in note 3, Fig. 2, p. 144; cat. 25, pp. 147–9; cat. 37, pp. 178–9; cat. 24, pp. 144–6.

21. Mineral deposits of silicaceous limestones or calcareous sandstones are common at many geographical locations. Materials such as these may have found application as canvas grounds in the seventeenth century; it is unlikely there would be a particular source or fixed constitution.

22. Other seventeenth-century canvas paintings with similar brown single grounds include works by Cavallino, Reni, Caravaggio, Pietro da Cortona, Salvator Rosa, Poussin, Sassoferrato, Velázquez and Zurbarán. Grounds of this type are best identified by XRD in conjunction with EDX analysis.

23. Even though the yellow component of azurite and yellow lake mixtures is vulnerable to fading and consequent colour change in the paint, this combination of pigments often retains a strongly green colour. This is probably because the azurite generally possesses a distinctly greenish tinge and also when it

is coarsely ground tends to require a large amount of lake pigment to make a workable paint film. There is therefore a 'reserve' of unfaded yellow colour in the paint layer.

24. Indigo identified by FTIR. The red lake as derived from a cochineal dyestuff was suggested by transmittance microspectrophotometry in the visible region of the spectrum.

25. Red lake glazes over translucent greens were widely used in Venetian painting, for example on Cima's altarpiece *The Incredulity of Saint Thomas* (NG 816), on panel, of 1504. See J. Dunkerton and A. Roy, 'The Technique and Restoration of Cima's "The Incredulity of S.Thomas"', *National Gallery Technical Bulletin*, 10, 1986, pp. 15–16 and Plates 2h–k, pp.12–13.

26. The panel for *Charity* consists of five oak planks with the grain running vertically, butt joined and dowelled. At some stage the panel had been thinned to 8mm and a cradle applied. This was removed during conservation treatment on acquisition in 1984. Details are recorded in the 'Conservation Dossier'.

27. The 'striped' *imprimatura* is very evident on Rubens's *Samson and Delilah* (NG 6461), and in other works by the artist, see Plesters, cited in note 13, Fig. 10, p. 37, and Fig. 14, p. 39. See also Fig. 13, p. 38, for *'Le Chapeau de Paille'* (NG 852), and Fig. 7, p. 34 for *A Lion Hunt* (NG 853.1). Some further notes on *imprimature* on panel of this kind can be found in N. van Hout, 'Meaning and Development of the Ground Layer in Seventeenth Century Painting', in *Looking Through Paintings: The Study of Painting Techniques and Materials in Support of Art Historical Research*, ed. by E. Hermens, Leids Kunsthistorisch Jaarboek XI, Leiden 1998, pp. 205–10.

28. Van Dyck's brilliant and expressive painting methods and brushwork were commented on quite early, a good example being R. de Piles's account in *Abrégé de la vie de peintres, avec des réflexion sur leurs Ouvrage, Et un Traité du Peintre parfait; De la connoissance de Desseins; De l'utilité des Estamps*, 2nd edn., Paris 1715, pp. 403–8, particularly p. 407.

29. Microscopic examination of samples of drapery paint suggested that two lake pigments, a red and a yellow, had been mixed to produce the desired colour. Examination of the dyestuffs present in samples by HPLC indicated that the red lake had been derived from a species of cochineal insect, in all probability the Mexican insect *Dactylopius coccus* Costa, although the chromatogram was somewhat obscured by the presence of the yellow pigment dyestuff. The yellow was present in quantities too small to be identified. See J. Kirby and R. White, 'The Identification of Red Lake Pigment Dyestuffs and a Discussion of Their Use', *National Gallery Technical Bulletin*, 17, 1996, pp. 56–80, particularly pp. 67, 73.

30. J. Wadum, 'The Antwerp Brand on Paintings on Panel', in Hermens ed., cited in note 27, pp. 179–90.

31. An account of standard-size panels and their supply is given in E. Van der Wetering, 'Painting Materials and Working Methods of the Young Rembrandt', *Rembrandt: The Painter at Work*, Amsterdam, 1997, pp. 11–17.

32. It is noticeable that in a number of drawings by Rubens, particularly landscape studies, there is often a small amount of red chalk drawing combined with a more extensive use of brown and black chalk and inks. This is particularly clear in *A Wagon fording a Stream* (NG 948; c.1635), in which the composition was begun roughly at the centre in red chalk and then elaborated in black chalk. Other examples are illustrated in C. Brown, *Making and Meaning: Rubens's Landscapes*, National Gallery exh. cat., London 1996, Figs. 84, 85, 88, 89 and 90, pp. 87–92. The technique is also used in figure groups and portraits, see J.S. Held, *Rubens: Selected Drawings*, Oxford 1986, pp. 19–23; plates 3, 6 and 7.

33. Samples from the Firle Van Dyck were examined at the National Gallery on behalf of International Fine Art Conservation Studios (Bristol), who restored the painting in 1993.

34. See Wheelock, Barnes and Held, cited in note 3, cat. 84, pp. 313–15; cat. 86, pp. 320–2.

35. Double grounds of this type for portraits on canvas continued in use in England until at least the late 1640s, for example in the work of Sir Peter Lely (1618–80). See E. Hendriks and K. Groen, 'Lely's Studio Practice', *Hamilton Kerr Institute Bulletin*, 2, 1994, pp. 21–37.

36. Green verditer is manufactured green basic copper carbonate, that is, artificial malachite, and possesses a spherulitic, even-sized particle form. The pigment is generally not very strong in colour but makes satisfactory greens when mixed with yellow pigments.

37. Identified by XRD. See also note 10.

38. Martin, cited in note 5, pp. 41–7.

39. The 'Conservation Dossier' for NG 1172 contains only a black and white photograph of the back of the original canvas of the picture and the stripes on the ticking are very dark. Since the painting has a lining canvas it is now impossible to gain access to the back of the original, but it is plausible that the stripes are in fact a very deep blue rather than black.

40. The canvas ticking for the Wilton House Van Dyck has dark blue stripes, where the threads have been dyed with indigo. Samples supplied in 1988 by International Fine Art Conservation Studios (Bristol) who undertook conservation work on the picture.

41. Calcium carbonate in the lower ground identified by EDX.

42. Martin, cited in note 5, p .42.

43. Martin, cited in note 5, p. 41.

44. No X-ray plates are available for the picture and the canvas weave was measured on the surface of the painting in places where the background paint is very thin. The thread count is therefore a rough estimate in this case.

45. Wheelock, Barnes and Held, cited in note 3, cat. 80, pp. 302–3; cat. 83, pp. 310–12.

46. Indigo identified by FTIR.

47. The identification of the birch pitch pigment is reported in R. White and J. Pilc, 'Analyses of Paint Media', *National Gallery Technical Bulletin*, 16, 1995, pp. 90–1 and p. 95.

Van Dyck's Paint Medium

RAYMOND WHITE

ANALYSIS of Van Dyck's paintings in the National Gallery Collection by gas chromatography (GC) alone, gas chromatography –mass spectrometry (GC–MS) and Fourier transform infra-red spectrometry (FTIR)–microscopy has shown that the artist used linseed oil to a very large extent; the results of analysis are tabulated in detail below. The sample of paintings examined is small compared with the painter's output as a whole, but it seems that for the paintings produced during the artist's period in England from 1632 until his death, linseed oil was his preferred medium. Walnut oil does occur, in yellow paint on the subject's shot pouch in *William Feilding, 1st Earl of Denbigh* (NG 5633) for example, but infrequently. Van Dyck used walnut oil to a greater extent in the paintings produced in Italy, and also in those like *Charity* (NG 6494), which were produced in Antwerp and Brussels after his return from Italy in 1627. Sometimes the oils were heat bodied; for example, heat-bodied walnut oil was used for George Gage's black robe in *Portrait of George Gage with Two Attendants* (NG 49), painted while the artist was in Rome. Heat-bodying in this instance would help to offset the tendency of organic black pigments to inhibit the drying process in oil paints, often causing paint film defects.

Van Dyck's discussion with de Mayerne on the use of an aqueous medium, such as gum or glue, for blues (and mixed greens), followed by a varnish, has been discussed above (see p. 15); in so far as it was possible to examine passages of blue or green paint, analysis of the paintings in the National Gallery Collection has revealed no evidence whatsoever of this practice.

Examination of the Table will show that Van Dyck added a trace of pine resin to the paint used for red glazed passages on drapery. In addition there is evidence for the use of heated pine products, typically softwood pitch, in brownish glaze paints from the *Portrait of George Gage*, *The Balbi Children* (NG 6502) and the *Equestrian Portrait of Charles I* (NG 1172). Heating resins or resin-containing materials

Plate 44 Anthony van Dyck, *William Feilding, 1st Earl of Denbigh* (NG 5633), *c.*1633–4. Canvas, 247.5 × 148.5 cm. Birch bark tar was used for the golden-brown glaze on the servant's tunic.

was a typical way to produce translucent, brown-black tars and pitches, which could be used in a similar way to asphaltum or bitumen.

Another variety of translucent brown, also produced by heating – not, in this case, resinous material, but wood or bark – was bistre, a form of tarry soot. It was used in *William Feilding, 1st Earl of Denbigh* (Plate 44).

Results of medium analysis

Picture	Sample	Medium
The Emperor Theodosius is forbidden by Saint Ambrose to enter Milan Cathedral NG 50 canvas c.1619–20	1. Thin warm glaze-like shadow-paint plus opaque black paint in shadow of step 2. Golden-coloured trimming on shoulder of Saint Ambrose's robe 3. Grey paint of architecture, upper right-hand edge 4. Red glaze paint of the Emperor Theodosius' robe	linseed oil, heat-bodied with traces of lower hopanes and pine resin[1] partially heat-bodied linseed oil linseed oil partially heat-bodied linseed oil + a little pine resin
Portrait of Cornelis van der Geest NG 52 oak c.1620	1. White impasto of ruff, to right of sitter's head 2. Fragment of greenish(?) brown/black from edge (added surround) 3. Black from shoulder, quite opaque	heat-bodied linseed oil partially heat-bodied linseed oil + a little pine resin[2] partially heat-bodied linseed oil
Portrait of a Woman and Child NG 3011 canvas c.1620–1	1. Sample of lower ground 2. Rich, wine-red glaze paint of drape, upper left-hand side 3. Shadow paint (opaque) of black satin dress, lower right-hand edge 4. Dark blue paint of distant landscape, to left of sitters	partially heat-bodied linseed oil[3] partially heat-bodied linseed oil + a little pine resin[4] heat-bodied linseed oil[5] linseed oil, partially heat-bodied[6]
Portrait of George Gage with Two Attendants NG 49 canvas probably 1622–3	1. Sleeve of black robe (sitter's left arm) 2. Right-hand attendant's brownish cloak (shoulder) 3. Cream-coloured impasto of distant sky, left-hand edge (above horizon) 4. Blue sleeve, attendant at extreme right	walnut oil, heat-bodied heat-bodied linseed oil with a trace of asphaltum or bitumen and a little heated pine resin[7] heat-bodied walnut oil partially heat-bodied linseed oil[8]
The Balbi Children NG 6502 canvas c.1625–7	1. Ground sample 2. Red glaze paint of right-hand child's dress (mid-tone) 3. Sky, mid-left-hand side 4. Flesh paint of right-hand child's left hand 5. Foliage of tree in background, seemingly dark brown	linseed oil[9] drying oil (linseed, or walnut – or a mixture of both) + traces of pine resin[10] linseed oil, no resin[11] partially heat-bodied walnut oil heat-bodied linseed oil with a little pine resin pitch[12]
Charity NG 6494 oak c.1627–8	1. Light brown ground + some dark blue underpaint and ultramarine glaze on top, from blue drape, left-hand side 2. Darker, more opaque paint from blue drape, left-hand side 3. Greenish-brown glaze, lower left-hand corner 4. Dark brown shadow of drapery 5. Dark brown glaze-like paint of background, left-hand side 6. Wine-red glaze paint of Charity's robe, right-hand side	partially heat-bodied walnut oil[13] partially heat-bodied walnut oil[14] heat-bodied linseed oil + lignitic earth(?)[15] analysis unsatisfactory through instrument failure[16] heat-bodied linseed oil with traces of pine resin and lignitic earth(?)[17] partially heat-bodied linseed oil + a little pine resin[18]
William Feilding, 1st Earl of Denbigh NG 5633 canvas c.1633–4	1. Green leaf, lower right-hand edge 2. Blue-green leaf, adjacent to sample 1 3. Yellow paint and warm glaze paint of back of servant's tunic 4. Brownish leaves, lower left-hand edge 5. Cool yellow highlight of shot pouch hanging at the Earl's right side	partially heat-bodied linseed oil partially heat-bodied linseed oil, rather lean, somewhat degraded medium[19] heat-bodied linseed (or linseed + walnut) oil with birch bark bistre[20] partially heat-bodied linseed oil heat-bodied walnut oil[21]

Picture	Sample	Medium
Carlo and Ubaldo see Rinaldo conquered by Love for Armida NG 877.2 oak 1634–5	1. White highlight of drape associated with putto, lower right-hand corner 2. Brown shadow, lower right-hand corner 3. Ground, from extreme edge, right-hand side	heat-bodied walnut oil partially heat-bodied linseed oil chalk ground and a protein-based binder by FTIR– microscopy
The Abbé Scaglia adoring the Virgin and Child NG 4889 canvas 1634–5	1. Dark green paint of drape behind the Virgin's left shoulder 2. Black(?), opaque outline paint from the Virgin's left shoulder, from a rather thick impasto stroke 3. Beige ground, from unpainted corner 4. Mustard impasto highlight of yellow cloud, to upper left of centre 5. Bright blue (ultramarine) sky, upper left 6. Dark blue of the Virgin's robe, with glaze paint 7. Purple-coloured sky, left-hand side 8. Warm brownish-black glaze paint of shadow from fold in pink sleeve of the Virgin's dress 9. Pink/red glaze paint of non-shadow area, adjacent to fold in pink sleeve of the Virgin's dress	linseed oil[22] partially heat-bodied linseed oil partially heat-bodied linseed oil heat-bodied linseed oil partially heat-bodied walnut oil heat-bodied linseed oil[23] partially heat-bodied drying oil[24] heat-bodied linseed oil + some pine resin + lignitic(?) earth pigment[25] partially heat-bodied linseed oil, with a trace of pine resin
Lady Elizabeth Thimbelby and Dorothy, Viscountess Andover[26] NG 6437 canvas *c.*1637	1. Warm glaze paint in darker shades of Lady Dorothy's yellow gown 2. Opaque, yellow principal layer of paint from Lady Dorothy's gown 3. Fragment of brown-red ground, with greyish priming 4. Dark semi-opaque brown of background, lower left 5. Red silk drape around winged putto 6. White of sleeve of Lady Dorothy's dress	linseed oil, heat-bodied + a little pine resin partially heat-bodied linseed oil[27] partially heat-bodied linseed oil[28] heat-bodied linseed oil with traces of asphaltum/bitumen[29] partially heat-bodied linseed oil + a little pine resin heat-bodied linseed oil
Equestrian Portrait of Charles I NG 1172 canvas *c.*1637–8	1. Warm white impasto stroke of distant white cloud just above horizon on left-hand edge 2. Warm brown glaze-stroke, over lower part of crimson silk garment of the equerry 3. Green leaves of foliage, lower right-hand side 4. Warm glaze paint toning over rock, lower right-hand side 5. Yellow highlight paint stroke of stirrup 6. Dark greyish blue of distant landscape, left-hand side 7. Pale crimson paint of equerry's sleeve 8. Rich blue sky, lower left-hand edge 9. Fragment of warm greyish ground	heat-bodied linseed oil heat-bodied linseed oil + a little pine resin linseed oil[30] heat-bodied linseed oil + some partially heated pine resin or pitch[31] heat-bodied linseed oil heat-bodied linseed oil[32] partially heat-bodied linseed oil, with a trace of pine resin heat-bodied linseed oil partially heat-bodied linseed oil
Lord John Stuart and his Brother, Lord Bernard Stuart[33] NG 6518 canvas *c.*1638	1. Brown-black paint of background, left-hand edge, above elbow 2. Yellow brocade wrap over upper arm of Lord John Stuart 3. Red-brown lining of drape, same figure 4. White highlight of Lord Bernard's grey silk sleeve 5. Black shadow in fold of silk jacket, same figure 6. Blue paint of cloak, same figure	linseed oil + birch pitch[34] walnut oil + birch pitch linseed oil walnut oil linseed oil + birch pitch linseed oil

Notes and References

1. Lower right-hand side. Components containing base peak of m/z 191 and seemingly lower norhopanes, possibly resulting from heated forms of asphaltic and bituminous pigments. See R. White, 'Brown and Black Organic Glazes, Pigments and Paints', *National Gallery Technical Bulletin*, 10, 1986, pp. 58–71.

2. This sample is from the later (1637) addition to the panel.

3. Infra-red microscopy indicated that drying oil was present as binding agent. The mineral content appeared to be calcite mixed with some silicates. This would appear to be some form of calcium carbonate-based silicaceous earth.

4. The lower part of this partially separated sample seemed more opaque (containing vermilion, principally), but with a little red lake. Here the medium proved to be partially heat-bodied linseed oil, with barely a trace of pine resin. This is in contrast to the lake-rich glaze paint above, with a more heat-bodied linseed oil and a more pronounced content of pine resin.

5. A fragment of upper ground or priming seemed to be present below this sample. However, its composition by FTIR–microscopy seemed to be different from that in sample 1 (the lower ground) in that it was a mixture of lead white and brown, with some black pigment, bound with drying oil.

6. There seems to be smalt in this and an isolated 'clump' of indigo particles, using FTIR–microscopy.

7. This sample consisted of a warm glaze paint (containing evidence of possibly heated asphaltic material, from lower hopane homologues), with a lower, brown, opaque paint and surprisingly an orange-red paint below this. An attempt was made to crudely separate the brown, more opaque paint and the orange-red material (vermilion + red lake pigments) below. GC–MS indicated the presence of a partially heat-bodied linseed oil, possibly with a trace of pine resin. However, the chromatogram also admitted evidence of a trace of larixol and another (possibly related) ketol. On balance one, or both, of the lower layers (perhaps relating to a previous composition on the added canvas section) seemed to possess paint media containing partially heat-bodied linseed oil with larch resin, or a mixture of larch and pine resins.

8. Seemed to have a greyish ground; the palmitate/stearate ester ratio value of the medium was on the linseed/walnut oil boundary (GC–MS analysis). However, linseed oil – partially heat-bodied – appeared to be the medium of the bulk of the principal layers of paint.

9. A cream-coloured ground and apparently a single layer. FTIR–microscopy indicated calcium carbonate and silica/silicate composition, presumably some form of carbonate-containing earth. Only drying oil was detected within the binding medium; there was no evidence of proteinaceous amide bands.

10. Partially heat-bodied drying oil, with a palmitate/stearate ester ratio of 2.0. This could be either linseed or walnut oil, possibly a mixture of both in view of the other results from this picture. Traces of pine resin were detected in the paint by GC–MS.

11. FTIR–microscopy revealed that some brownish-grey material present was discoloured smalt in a drying oil medium.

12. FTIR–microscopy showed a rather dark organic matrix, some brownish particles and some verdigris particles. Heat-bodied linseed oil was identified by GC–MS. From the GC–MS total ion chromatogram, evidence of a trace of simonellite (and retene, too) suggested a minor addition of partially tarred softwood resin/pitch. This would seem an unsuitable component, if the leaves were intended to be green originally. The resin was distributed throughout the medium rather than added as a 'copper resinate' pigment.

13. FTIR–microscopy confirmed that indigo pigment was present in the dark blue layer, with a medium of drying oil. The pale blue ultramarine glaze appeared to contain a drying oil binder as well. No layers of glue or gum-like materials were detected as potential isolating material around the ultramarine pigment.

14. FTIR–microscopy confirmed indigo pigment to be present in the sample. Although there was no sign of a distinct boundary, nevertheless subtraction of the contribution from the 'core' of the pigment, and partial removal of the (drying oil) medium-rich areas, left a spectral residue with a certain similarity to that encountered in polysaccharidic materials. This may represent 'gummy' impurities brought down on the surface of the crude indigo particles – equally, it may represent a treatment of that pigment with a plant-gum extract. Notably, this was not found to be the case for the ultramarine particles present in sample 1.

15. This sample appeared to contain green and brown pigments, possibly Cassel earth. Following analysis by GC–MS there was an indication of the use of heat-bodied linseed oil: no resin, softwood pitch or any of the usual hopane homologues were detected in this sample. Interestingly, a subsequent ion scan for m/z of 109 revealed a vestigial peak of almost identical retention time to that component found in sample 5 (see note 17 below).

16. This sample of paint appeared to be a dark yellow-brown glaze, with a few opaque particles and traces of red lake beneath. FTIR–microscopy indicated the medium to be essentially drying oil.

17. 7-oxodehydroabietic acid indicated the presence of a conifer resin (most probably from *Pinus* sp.). Traces of three components, with (B⁺) m/z = 109 and (M⁺) m/z = 262 with peaks at m/z = 191, 219, (B⁺) m/z = 259 (M⁺) m/z = 274 (minimal), and (B⁺) m/z = 95, (M⁺) m/z = 276 with a strong m/z = 247, were present. These components would appear to correspond with fichtelite and possibly the dihydro- and tetrahydrorimuenes, which might result from the inclusion of some form of lignitic earth.

18. A tiny fragment of double ground was present at the bottom of this and had broken away. A warm cream-coloured ground appeared to contain oil, but a cooler, greyish lower ground gave some indication of protein amide bands, probably glue, upon examination by FTIR–microscopy.

19. This paint had a somewhat blanched appearance. There appeared to be some particles of yellow lake here, too.

20. It was not possible to separate the warm glaze-like paint from the yellow, more opaque paint. GC–MS indicated that the medium was composed of (essentially) heat-bodied linseed oil, but that the palmitate/stearate (P/S) ratio was at the upper limit for that material, in contrast to the other samples from this work containing linseed oil. In view of the medium analysis for sample 5, a mixture of linseed and walnut oils (the latter possibly originating from the opaque yellow paint) appears likely. Traces of betulinic acid were detected and another triterpenoid acid, possibly betulonic acid from its fragmentation pattern. This might suggest the presence of a heavily oxidised birch bark tar component or a birch bark bistre, but there are complications in the form of rather polar components which seemed to produce rather poor chromatographic and spectral peaks following GC–MS analysis. They were resolved – to some extent – only after acidification of the TMTFTH-treated remnants and examination by gradient elution, reversed phase HPLC (high performance liquid chromatography). These components appeared to be phenolic and correspond to syringyl and ferulyl fragments, most likely resulting from the inclusion of degraded lignin in the material. From this we may infer that actual birch wood (from which betulin is absent, but lignins, based on ferulic and syringic component polymers, are present) was mixed with the corresponding bark, from which the betulin and its subsequent oxidation products, but not the lignin, originate.

21. Some slightly opalescent inclusions, within the body of the paint medium, were examined by FTIR–microscopy and were found to be occluded regions of fatty acid carboxylates. Given the asymmetric carbonyl stretching frequency, measured as $c.1510$–12 cm^{-1}, with the corresponding symmetric carbonyl stretch at $c.1400$–7 cm^{-1}, it would seem that this material represents occlusions of metal soaps. Lead soaps appear to have a lower asymmetric carbonyl stretching frequency than the corresponding alkali metal soaps, which appear in the mid-1500s cm^{-1} region.

22. FTIR indicated the presence of indigo dyestuff as well as some particles of yellow lake. This was mixed with lead-tin yellow pigment, to produce green.

23. Both samples 5 and 6 contained ultramarine, with the addition of some indigo in the latter. Despite careful examination by FTIR–microscopy, no evidence of a proteinaceous or a gum-based medium or pigment-isolating layer was found to support the use of such materials in conjunction with ultramarine-based paints

as mentioned by de Mayerne (see p. 15 of this *Bulletin*).

24. The palmitate/stearate ester ratio measured by GC–MS was at the walnut/linseed oil boundary – possibly a mixture of the two is present, with linseed dominant.

25. A trace of a component with a mass spectrum resembling fichtelite was detected by GC–MS.

26. These represent further results, obtained by GC–MS and FTIR–microscopy on fragments remaining from the 1977 (GC analysis only) sampling campaign. These media results were reported in J. Mills and R. White, 'Organic Analysis in the Arts: Some Further Paint Medium Analyses', *National Gallery Technical Bulletin*, 2, 1978, p. 74. Linseed oil was identified in yellow highlights of Lady Dorothy's dress and in a white sleeve as well as in a green drape in the background.

27. Two slightly opalescent inclusions within the body of the paint medium were examined by FTIR–microscopy and were found to be occluded regions of fatty acid carboxylates. See note 21, above.

28. FTIR–microscopy pointed to the use of a drying oil medium in both ground and priming layers.

29. This sample area corresponded with sample 3 (dark brown of background, lower left edge) in the 1977 campaign. At the time, using GC only, it was felt that some asphaltic material might be present in view of poorly resolved high retention time peaks emerging after the main chromatographic run. Lower hopane homologues were identified by GC–MS in the current study, which suggest the presence of a heat-treated asphaltum or bitumen.

30. This paint appeared slightly blanched and discoloured.

31. Inferred from the presence of dehydroabietic and 7-oxodehydroabietic acids, simonellite and traces of retene in this sample, following GC–MS examination.

32. FTIR–microscopy indicated the presence of some smalt in this sample.

33. A detailed study of this picture was reported in R. White and J. Pilc, 'Analyses of Paint Media', *National Gallery Technical Bulletin*, 16, 1995, pp. 90–1 and note 24, p. 95.

34. Some signs of paint shrinkage in this area.

Rubens's *Peace and War*

ASHOK ROY

THE TRADITIONAL title given to Rubens's great allegorical composition in the National Gallery, 'Peace and War' (NG 46; Plate 1), refers to the purpose of the picture as a gift to Charles I and represents Rubens's aims as envoy of Philip IV of Spain in peace negotiations between England and Spain. The National Gallery Flemish School Catalogue gives the full title as: *Minerva protects Pax from Mars ('Peace and War')*. The picture was painted in 1629–30, most probably towards the end of Rubens's stay in England, from where he returned to Antwerp in March 1630, having been knighted by Charles. The circumstances of the creation of 'Peace and War', a detailed description of the subject matter and a hypothetical analysis of the evolution of the composition have been given by Gregory Martin in a full catalogue entry compiled in 1970.[1] In his account, Martin describes the complex make-up of the canvas support, which is discussed in more detail below, and identifies certain of the figures as members of the family of Sir Balthazar Gerbier (1592–1667) with whom Rubens stayed when he was in London.

The subject matter can be described briefly as follows. The helmeted woman at the centre is Minerva and she is pushing away the figure of Mars dressed in armour; the woman to his right is probably a Fury and to her right, in the sky, is a Harpy. The putto in the sky above carries a caduceus and olive wreath referring to peace and harmony. The nude woman at the centre is the goddess Pax; she is feeding from her breast the child Plutus, god of wealth. Martin identifies the boy holding the torch as Hymen, who is crowning the girl shown in profile to suggest that marriage is in accord with the state of peace. The satyr is offering the children a cornucopia of fruit, symbolising plenty. It has been suggested that the satyr and the two women at the left refer to Bacchus's entourage and this would account also for the leopard in the foreground, but the significance of these figures has not been established firmly.

It has not been doubted that the whole composition is an autograph painting by Rubens, but the complex make-up of the canvas support requires some explanation. 'Peace and War' was the subject of a preliminary technical investigation in 1969, but because of the presence of an old, thick, heavily discoloured varnish, it was not possible then to evaluate the layer structure of the picture. Subsequently, in 1984–7, the picture was cleaned and restored by Anthony Reeve in the Conservation Department of the National Gallery and this allowed a more searching technical study and some paint analysis to be carried out (see Appendix).[2] At the same time, a full X-ray mosaic of the painting was made (Fig. 1), which shows something of the structure of the support as well as the ground and paint layers.[3]

The support for 'Peace and War' is made up of seven separate pieces of canvas, the largest of which are two central pieces each about 136 cm high, by 99 cm and 114 cm wide, joined vertically, on which the principal sections of the composition are painted: the figures of Minerva, Mars, Pax, Hymen and most of the figure of the satyr with the cornucopia at the left, as well as the children and the foreground putto, all in half-length. The field of the composition is extended on to the additions arranged around the central rectangular pair of joined canvases as shown in the diagram (Fig. 2). This is a slightly modified version of the construction given by Martin, in which was omitted an unrecorded additional join in the right-hand extension, running horizontally about 64 cm from the line of the lower edge.[4] Thread counts taken from X-ray plates show that the two central canvas pieces have the same weave, while those of the additions differ slightly and are marginally finer.[5]

With an elaborate and complex support such as this, to account for the evolution of the composition becomes a key question. Several possibilities suggest themselves. First, that the support was made up in its entirety as a preliminary to painting, and that the composition was worked up as a whole with the present dimensions and format in Rubens's mind at the outset. Second, that Rubens began the painting on

Plate 1 Peter Paul Rubens, *Minerva protects Pax from Mars ('Peace and War')* (NG 46), 1629–30. Canvas, 203.5 × 298 cm.

Fig. 1 Rubens, *'Peace and War'*, X-ray composite of the whole.

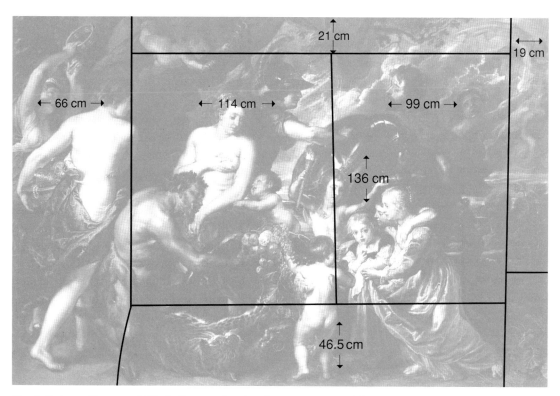

Fig. 2 Rubens, *'Peace and War'*, diagram showing the construction of the canvas support.

the central rectangular portion of the support, and brought this part of the composition to an advanced degree of finish, or perhaps completed it. The field of the painting was then, it can be hypothesised, extended with new strips of canvas joined to the central pieces and the composition elaborated in the larger format. Third, that Rubens produced a finished independent picture on the central portion, which was subsequently extended and the painted additions completed by another hand. The technical evidence, as well as the provenance of the picture (it was recorded in Charles I's collection in a catalogue of 1637–40),[6] are against the third course of events, while examination of the support suggests that the first possibility – an initial plan for the painting in its present format – is not the likely explanation. The second possibility, one deduced also by Gregory Martin, although without technical data to support it, appears to be the correct interpretation of Rubens's painting procedure in this case.

During the process of painting it was not uncommon for Rubens to adapt or enlarge the support. In fact, he is known to have adopted this method of working for paintings on both panel and canvas. At least two landscapes on wood panel in the National Gallery Collection, *Peasants with Cattle by a Stream in a Woody Landscape* ('The Watering Place') (NG 4815; *c.*1620) and *A Landscape with a Shepherd and his Flock* (NG 157; *c.*1638), show evidence of enlargement of the panel support during the painting process.[7]

However, certain of Rubens's paintings, particularly his landscapes, but other compositions as well, have structurally complex panel supports made up from a large number of elements which were not added in the course of execution, nor as the result of later phases of composition. The large pair of pendant landscapes, painted probably in 1636, *An Autumn Landscape with a View of Het Steen in the Early Morning* (NG 66) and *Landscape with a Rainbow* (London, Wallace Collection) are good examples, and there are others.[8] The use of supports assembled from a number of separate pieces of canvas in arrangements more complex than simple parallel joins between strips is also known for pictures of this period by other artists, for example Jacob Jordaens's *Portrait of Govaert van Surpele(?) and his Wife* probably of 1636–8 (NG 6293; overall dimensions: 213 × 189 cm), which is made up of six pieces of canvas.

In *'Peace and War'* the various sections of canvas are sewn together. The seams, and the threads which make them up, are clearly visible in X-ray photographs (see Fig. 3); the structure of the seams

Fig. 3 Rubens, *'Peace and War'*. X-ray detail, lower right corner, showing the seams for the right-hand and lower canvas additions and the overlap of ground layers from the additions to the main field.

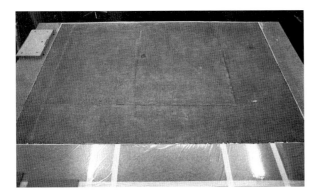

Fig. 4 Rubens, *'Peace and War'*. Reverse of the original canvas assembly, after removal of the old lining canvas, showing the seams.

was evident after the removal of an old lining canvas in 1983. It was evident, also, from the back of the original canvas assembly (Fig. 4), as well as from the X-ray image, that the central two pieces of canvas had been mounted independently on a stretcher or strainer, since the canvas weave is noticeably cusped and distorted around the edges. This observation points to an expansion of the format of the painting from a finished, or largely finished, core, but clearer indications of the correctness of this interpretation arise from the nature and disposition of the ground layers on different parts of the canvas support as

revealed in the X-ray image and by paint cross-sections.

The composite X-ray image of the painting shows considerably greater overall radiographic density on all the canvas additions arranged around the central core (see Figs. 1 and 3). Since there is a relatively unbroken peripheral zone of radio-absorbent material, it must result from greater X-ray density in the grounds on the additions. Cross-sections from the central portion of the picture show that each of the main centre strips of canvas bears the same double ground. This consists of a lower, fairly thick reddish-brown translucent layer composed largely of calcium carbonate tinted with red earth, and over this, a second exceedingly thin upper priming of a warmish mid grey-brown, only just concealing the red-brown layer below (Plate 2). The ground layers on the additions are consistent in constitution from place to place on the structure, and, as on the centre, are made up of a double-layered system. The lower ground on the canvas extensions is a moderately thick layer of earth pigment of a strong mid red-brown and over this there is a substantial upper ground, light beige in colour. This second ground, probably mainly responsible for the radio-absorbency seen in the X-ray image, consists of lead white tinted with a little black pigment (mainly lampblack) and a fine red earth; it also contains occasional clumps of aggregate particles of yellow ochre (Plate 3).[9] The thickness of this upper ground layer and its particular constitution make it possible to detect and recognise the layer wherever it occurs in paint samples, and the spatial extent of its application is similarly easy to map on the picture and on the X-ray. The X-ray image also shows broad curving marks in this upper ground, suggesting that it was applied with a palette knife.

The band of additional X-ray density imparted by the upper beige ground can be seen to overlap the seams of the additions around the entire profile of the central canvas structure: by about 2–4 cm at top and bottom additions, by 5–7 cm at the junction of the right-hand addition, and by 6–9 cm at the left-hand addition. Cross-sections taken through the full layer structure at these zones of overlap (Plate 4) are therefore crucial in understanding the order of events in the construction of the assembly. Examination of the layer structure at several sample points reveals the following sequence, from the canvas upwards:

1. The double ground present on the centrally joined (core) canvases

2. A layer, or layers, of paint: the pictorial layers of the first, core, stage

3. The upper (beige) ground of the extension strips
4. A second layer or sequence of layers of paint: the present surface paint. In some places, although not everywhere, these correspond to the colours beneath the surface found at 2.

The obvious inference is that the central core composition originally enjoyed an independent existence, on a stretcher or strainer, and had been taken to some degree of completion as a painting. This picture had then been demounted and new canvas sewn around the edges, making use of the turnovers of the central portion to attach the additions. The excess canvas at the back of the seams was trimmed away at some stage, but it is not known when this was done. It remains to be established whether the strips of canvas used to extend the field had the lower red-brown ground in place before these were attached, but the cross-sections seem to suggest that both stages of priming on the additions were carried out after they were in place.[10] The thick, upper beige-coloured ground was evidently applied in a single layer over the lower ground on the additions, and spread across the seams to disguise the joins.

The differences in colour and texture between the grounds on the centre portion and the extended parts have probably become more pronounced with age, and this has resulted in a cooler and flatter look to the composition in the extended areas. These passages are in general freer and more sketchily worked than the tightly focused and highly wrought core composition, and the ground colour influences the tonality at the periphery more than at the centre (Plate 5). It is not clear whether Rubens chose a rather differently coloured ground for the extensions, with the intention of exploiting its tone as part of his plan for the final, enlarged composition. But the differences brought about by ageing and other changes with time have certainly had their effect on the appearance and condition of the different parts of the picture.

Gregory Martin argued that *'Peace and War'* had been evolved by Rubens from a central composition, which involved half-length figures of the group of children at the right and the winged putto in the foreground. Support for this theory rested on the existence of several preliminary sketches for the central composition and sketches for individual figures, none of which included full-length studies .[11] He also suggested an intermediate stage of the design, worked up as a *modello*, now lost, the composition of which was further altered in the execution of the central part of *'Peace and War'*. Whether or not this *modello* existed, it is clear from the number of drawn

Plate 2 Rubens, *'Peace and War'*. Paint cross-section from the brightest blue sky just above Minerva's helmet, from the central part of the composition, consisting of ultramarine over a thin brown underpaint. The double ground on the core canvases consists of a translucent reddish-brown lower layer and a thin warm mid-grey-brown on top. Original magnification 350×; actual magnification 210×.

Plate 3 Rubens, *'Peace and War'*. Paint cross-section from the upper arm of the woman carrying treasure at the left of the composition. This shows a single layer of flesh paint over the double ground present on the canvas additions. This double ground consists of a mid-red-brown layer of earth pigment and a thick, light beige upper ground layer. Original magnification 275×; actual magnification 165×.

Plate 4 Rubens, *'Peace and War'*. Cross-section of dark green landscape a few centimetres to the left of the seam joining the right-hand canvas addition to the main field. The lower double ground of the main field is visible at the base of the sample; there is then a layer of dark blue-green paint representing the initial landscape on the core composition. This is covered by a thick layer of beige upper ground that overlaps the seam from the added strip of canvas at the right. The top dark green layer is the surface landscape paint, concealing the junction. Original magnification 320×; actual magnification 195×.

Plate 5 Rubens, '*Peace and War*'. Detail of the children on the right, showing the junction of the addition and the main field just below the older girl's hands.

studies that Rubens's preparation of the design was careful and considered.

One can conjecture that the success of Rubens's diplomatic mission to England, and the benefits to his reputation and standing which resulted from it, called for a grander and more imposing gesture to the King than Rubens perhaps initially conceived. This would account for the expansion of the format of the painting and the evident haste in which the outer parts of the composition were finished. The paint structures show that the enlarged painting was finished soon after the central core had been painted, and many areas along the joins show brushstrokes and whole passages worked back over the seam on to the main, central field. This is particularly evident in the flesh of the satyr's back, in the orange and gold dress of the girl to the right, particularly in the highlights, and in the smoothly painted shoulder of the woman at the left carrying the bowl of treasure.[12] On a smaller scale, with more attention to detail, similar brushstrokes worked across the joins can be seen in the leopard's claws and in the landscape to the right.

As we have seen, complicated and elaborate supports are common in Rubens's work and it is often difficult to judge whether their enlargement from a central design was projected at an early stage. Although technical evidence seems to support the view that the composition of '*Peace and War*' was elaborated later, it cannot be ruled out that Rubens conceived from the outset the grander, larger composition that we see today, and that his idiosyncratic way of working required two quite distinct stages of design and painting.

Appendix: The materials of '*Peace and War*'

Ground layers

The central joined canvases carry a double ground consisting of a red-brown lower layer of calcium carbonate and a red earth, with a very thin warm mid-grey-brown on top. This upper layer consists of lead white and earth pigments. The canvas strips that extend the field of the central 'core' also carry double grounds. Here the lower layer is a darker red-brown containing red earth and calcium carbonate. A thick grey ground over this consists of lead white, with a little lampblack, coarser black pigment, fine red earth and yellow ochre.

Flesh paints

The system of flesh painting is straightforward. Two layers are evident where Rubens continued to work the paint over the joins in the enlarged composition, for example in the figure of the satyr. The clearest pink tones contain small quantities of vermilion mixed with lead white, while fine red earth is included for the rather browner half-shadows. Cool shadows result from the addition of small amounts of black pigment, Cassel earth and, occasionally, azurite, to the flesh paints. The yellowest tones contain yellow ochre.

Draperies

Red Minerva's bright red drapery is painted in vermilion with a thin red glaze of a faintly orange-red coloured lake, or mixture of lakes. Mars' duller red drapery also contains vermilion (partially darkened at the surface) over an underpaint of red-brown earth mixed with red lake. Pax's drapery contains a mixture of red lake pigments, possibly madder combined with cochineal.[13]

Lilac The grey-lilac drapery of the bacchante(?) with the tambourine, at the left, consists of a mixture of lead white, charcoal black and red lake pigment. No blue pigment is present.

Yellow and orange The golden-yellow to orange-brown dress, worn by the girl to the right, consists of a combination of opaque and translucent pigments according to colour and shadow value. The palest impasto highlights are pure lead-tin yellow ('type I'), while a more orange colour is imparted by the addition of vermilion. Translucency and darker tones in the shadows result from the use of yellow lake, translucent golden ochre and Cassel earth. (The method of painting and materials are closely similar to those used by Rubens for Delilah's golden drapery in *Samson and Delilah*, NG 6461.[14])

Green The embroidered drapery around the waist of the woman carrying treasure at the left owes its lightest green colours to a combination of lead-tin yellow mixed with white and mineral azurite. The bluest areas consist of azurite scumbled over a solid mid-green underlayer, while the very deep blue-green shadows contain indigo and charcoal black. In the most translucent deep greens, the paint contains yellow lake in addition to azurite.

Black The deep blue-black of the bodice of the little girl facing out of the composition is painted in a mixture of charcoal black and mineral azurite, with a little added white.

Background setting

The sky contains natural ultramarine (rather blanched), and ultramarine over azurite mixed with white and black occurs in the bluest parts of the distant landscape at the centre of the composition. The dark green foliage at the right is painted in azurite, lead-tin yellow, black and white; dark landscape details at the right consist of azurite, black pigment and yellow lake.

Notes and references

1. G. Martin, *National Gallery Catalogues: Flemish School, 1600–1900*, London 1970, pp. 116–25.

2. 'Peace and War' was relined in 1983 at the time of the conservation treatment. Full details of treatment are recorded in the National Gallery 'Conservation Dossier'. A series of paint samples was taken for microscopical examination and analysis by standard methods in use in the Scientific Department of the National Gallery. These techniques of analysis included optical microscopy of cross-sections and dispersed samples, SEM–EDX, XRD and GC–MS.

3. The full X-ray image of the picture enables the structure of the support and all its joins to be examined. Some earlier X-ray plates had been taken in 1947, but these were too few for the complexity of the support to be assessed.

4. A diagram of the structure of the support is given in an appendix to the Flemish School Catalogue, see G. Martin, cited in note 1. This shows a narrow addition at the right side of the picture joined to a larger additional strip at the right. However, the narrow strip is in fact a crease in the canvas from an old stretcher and a similar crease can be seen at the left side of the picture. The published diagram does not show the horizontal join present in the right-hand addition.

5. The thread count on the central pair of canvases is the same for each – approximately 10 × 10 threads per cm. The weave of the extension strips of canvas is on average 10 × 11 threads per cm.

6. See G. Martin, cited in note 1, p. 117.

7. C. Brown, *Making and Meaning: Rubens's Landscapes*, exh. cat., National Gallery, London 1996, pp. 99–102; see also *idem*, C. Brown and A. Reeve, 'Appendix: The Structure of Rubens's Landscapes', pp. 116–21.

8. C. Brown, cited in note 7, p. 99. A Rubens panel painting in Dresden, *An Old Man with a Brazier*, is painted on an extraordinarily complex assemblage of small pieces of wood, including triangular-shaped joints and inserts. A whole series of these joins is at the centre of the composition, and it is inconceivable that the picture underwent an expansion of the panel from a central core. Similarly, although the support is less elaborate, the National Gallery *Portrait of Susanna Lunden (?) ('Le Chapeau de Paille')* (NG 852) has joins in the panel which pass through the main part of the figure of the sitter. This too is unlikely to have undergone expansion from a smaller format.

9. The upper grey ground on the additions contains scattered clumps of yellow ochre of a strong dark yellow colour which consist of large numbers of fine particles in aggregation. The presence of this pigment enables this ground layer to be recognised readily in samples.

10. Examination of cross-sections taken from the canvas additions shows that the two layers of the double ground are often seen to merge. This implies that the lower ground was still soft, or not fully dried, when the upper layer was applied, and that they were, therefore, probably applied at the same time.

11. G. Martin, cited in note 1, pp. 118–19.

12. Examination of the upper paint layers that traverse the joins in the support shows that Rubens worked back across the composition to unite the central section with the additions. This is particularly evident if the craquelure pattern in the paint that crosses the joins is examined and it is quite clear that these layers have dried, aged and cracked in precisely the same way on each side of the junctions in the support. Examination of the layer structure in the central part of the composition, for example in the flesh of the satyr at the left, shows that Rubens continued to work on the centre after the additions had been applied.

13. J. Kirby and R. White, 'The Identification of Red Lake Pigment Dyestuffs and a Discussion of their Use', *National Gallery Technical Bulletin*, 17, 1996, p. 67; Table 2, p. 73, and note 103, p. 80.

14. See J. Plesters, ' "Samson and Delilah": Rubens and the Art and Craft of Painting on Panel', *National Gallery Technical Bulletin*, 7, 1983, pp. 39–40, 45 and 48–9.

The Rubens Studio and the
Drunken Silenus supported by Satyrs

LARRY KEITH

SINCE its acquisition in 1871, the National Gallery's *Drunken Silenus supported by Satyrs* (NG 853; Plate 1) has prompted considerable discussion of both its authorship and its relationship to the production of the Rubens studio. A number of theories have been advanced in support of a wide range of attributions, including the suggestions that it is an essentially autograph Rubens, a collaboration of Van Dyck, Snijders and others following a design by Rubens, or a largely anonymous studio collaboration.[1] The recent restoration of the picture in the Conservation Department has allowed the opportunity to consider the questions surrounding its authorship and execution afresh in the context of a collaborative technical investigation with the Scientific Department.[2]

The organisation and functioning of the Rubens studio have always been key issues in the consideration of his output, and have remained so from the artist's own time throughout the subsequent history of Rubens scholarship.[3] Enough contemporary documentation exists, including documentation on individual paintings (much of which has come from Rubens's own correspondence) as well as more general descriptive evidence, to construct a reasonably broad outline of his studio's workings. There has, however, always been a certain tension between Rubens scholars who favour an extraordinarily prolific genius, and those who have seen a highly systematic and streamlined factory-like production of paintings. An exact definition will probably always be somewhat elusive, not least because of the fundamentally different idea of authorship, more focused on the invention or conception of an image and therefore less precise about its actual execution, found in much seventeenth-century painting.[4]

Nonetheless it seems clear that Rubens set about creating a large studio with many assistants, no doubt in some degree influenced by examples he had seen in his Italian travels, as he established his practice in Antwerp in 1609. Although his position as a painter at the court of the Spanish Netherlands exempted him from the normal practice of registering his assistants with the Guild of Saint Luke, some idea of the scale of his operation is indicated by the fact that by 1611 he wrote of the necessity of refusing more than one hundred applications from hopeful students.[5]

The assistants in the studio ranged from relatively unformed students to semi-independent collaborators employed as specialist painters of specific compositional elements such as animals, landscape, or still-life elements, while at least one artist, Anthony van Dyck, eventually enjoyed even more independent authority for the supervision of specific projects.[6] In general, however, Rubens's assistants were more commonly engaged in providing copies and replicas of finished paintings, or in the enlargement or preliminary laying-in of compositions previously executed by Rubens in drawings or more worked-up oil sketches – preparatory work which was corrected or finished in varying degrees by Rubens himself in the final full-scale painting. This sort of division of labour was practised quite openly by the studio, and afforded Rubens a great amount of flexibility; the extent of his participation on any one project often depended on the importance or cost of the commission. In his famous letter of 28 April 1618 to Sir Dudley Carleton, the English connoisseur and ambassador to The Hague, Rubens outlined the different degrees of his participation on a given painting, and by extension the commensurate range of price. He also gave Carleton more specific examples of collaborative effort, describing in the same letter his *Prometheus Bound* of 1618 (Fig. 2), now in the Philadelphia Museum of Art, as a wholly autograph work with the exception of the eagle, which was painted by Frans Snijders, and a scene of leopards, nymphs and satyrs as being entirely by his hand 'except a most beautiful landscape, done by a master skilful in that department'. But of *Achilles discovered among the Daughters of Lycomedes* (Fig. 3), he says that it was painted by his assistant and retouched by

Plate 1 Peter Paul Rubens, *Drunken Silenus supported by Satyrs* (NG 853), *c.*1620. Canvas, 133.5 × 197 cm.

Fig. 1 *Drunken Silenus supported by Satyrs* (NG 853). Composite X-radiograph.

Fig. 2 Peter Paul Rubens, *Prometheus Bound*, 1618. Canvas, 242.6 × 209.5 cm. Philadelphia Museum of Art (w 1950-3-3).

Fig. 3 Peter Paul Rubens, *Achilles discovered among the Daughters of Lycomedes*, *c.*1616–18. Canvas, 246 × 261 cm. Madrid, Prado Museum (no. 127).

himself.[7] Dr Otto Sperling, visiting the studio around 1620, gave a more general description of what presumably was also a common practice, the execution of a commission with a significantly smaller degree of participation by Rubens in the painting process:

> We saw a vast room without windows, but lighted by a large opening in the ceiling. There were gathered a good number of young painters who worked on different pieces of which Rubens had given them a chalk drawing touched here and there with colours. The young men had to completely execute these paintings, which were then finished off with line and colour by Rubens himself.[8]

This description accords well with the tradition behind the accounts given by Bellori, de Piles and Sandrart, all of which were written in the late seventeenth century and all of which describe a systematic use of assistants for copying and underpainting in the Rubens studio.[9]

The various attributions given to the National Gallery *Drunken Silenus* effectively cover the range of possibilities for Rubens's own participation in the painting as described by himself and his contemporaries; scholars have quite sensibly followed the documented categories as guides for the evaluation of relatively undocumented works like the National Gallery picture. This evaluation was formerly based almost entirely on traditional art-historical concepts of stylistic affinities as determined by the connoisseurship of the viewer, but in recent decades more technical information has played a larger part in the formation of an attribution.[10] The recent examination of the *Silenus*, which has made use of analytical techniques not available for earlier studies, has provided additional relevant, if not conclusive, information, and itself raises interesting questions concerning the still-evolving relationship between more objective data and aesthetic judgement.

The picture was painted over a double ground, comprising a grey oil-paint layer of lead white and lampblack over a lower layer of chalk in oil (Plate 2).[11] The grey tone provided by the ground was used extensively in the final painting, either completely covered or thinly veiled; it provides the basic colour for Silenus' beard and sideburns, and is only slightly worked over in the fur trim of the cloak over Silenus' legs (Plates 3 and 5). Perhaps less deliberately, it is also visible between numerous painted contours, for example between the young bacchante's right armpit and the head of the adjacent satyr. This type of feature could conceivably support the argument that the picture remains unfinished, but it would also be wholly in keeping with the piecemeal and sometimes collaborative execution common in Rubens's studio.

Examination of the X-radiograph of the picture certainly strengthens the impression of a highly organised and systematised painting method (Fig. 1). For so elaborate a multi-figure composition, there are no major pentimenti of any consequence; a readjustment of the contour of Silenus' left shoulder and some minor alterations in the hanging foliage around his head are the only notable changes. Apart from a drawing now in Chantilly, of a *Drunken Silenus* (or *Hercules*) (Fig. 4), which anticipates the general pose of the principal figure, there are no other known preparatory works for the National Gallery picture. The nature of its execution, however, with its fluently interlocking figures, open contours, and extensive final use of the ground colour, points clearly to the existence of a fully evolved compositional study by Rubens which was used as the pattern for the execution of the full-size painting, whoever the painter or painters might have been. No preliminary drawing is visible with the naked eye, and while many different materials might have been used to sketch in the composition, including charcoal, chalk, or brushed drawing in a variety of pigments and media, whatever may remain is no longer detectable with X-radiographic or infra-red techniques.[12]

Before evaluating the painting technique of the upper layers it is first necessary to describe a few potentially confusing changes in the condition of some of the materials. For example, while a purplish-coloured red lake pigment used extensively in Silenus' flesh, and readily visible along the arm and elbow of the satyr behind him, remains strongly coloured, another red lake has faded almost entirely from several areas of the picture (Plate 4).[13] Seemingly more brownish-red in tone, this colour was used extensively in the eye sockets of both satyrs and the old bacchante, as well as in other more shadowed areas of their faces and flesh, and its disappearance has left a chalky, blanched colour that disrupts and in some cases inverts the intended tonal modelling. This effect is particularly marked where the pigment has been used alongside other originally similar colours, whether organic or inorganic pigments, which have remained largely unchanged. Also, the rather amorphous and unmodelled appearance of the old bacchante's dress is probably largely due to the instability of its major component pigment, indigo,

Plate 2 *Drunken Silenus*. Cross-section detail from the line of shadow above the young satyr's wrist consisting of red lake pigment mixed with vermilion and a little red earth and black. There is severe fading in the lake pigment, most evident in the upper part of the paint layer. The double ground comprising a lower layer of chalk in oil and an upper layer of lead white with a little lampblack is visible beneath the paint layer. Original magnification 320×; actual magnification 195×.

Plate 3 *Drunken Silenus*. Detail showing the use of exposed ground to provide the basic tone for the fur trim of Silenus' cloak.

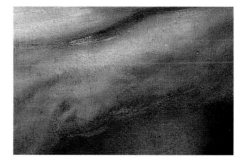

Plate 4 *Drunken Silenus*. Detail showing faded red lakes, visible as chalky grey streaks along the contours of the arm of Silenus' supporting satyr.

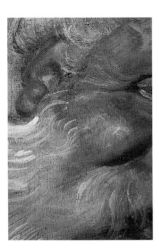

Plate 5 *Drunken Silenus*. Detail showing the use of the exposed grey ground to give the basic colour in the sideburns and beard; the jagged right contour of the upper ear, which appears to have been covered over with grey paint of the sideburn, is actually placed alongside ground layer left in reserve to provide the basic colour of the hair.

Fig. 4 Peter Paul Rubens, *Drunken Silenus* (or *Hercules*). Chalk reinforced with ink on paper. Detail from a sheet of drawings. 27 × 30 cm. Chantilly, Musée Condé.

which has faded markedly where it was used thinly, and where it was built up more thickly seems to have suffered a darkening of the medium, and subsequent browning of the paint layer.

Apart from these changes the picture remains in good condition for its age, and contains many passages of high and unaltered quality. And, while certainly not on the same level as a largely autograph Rubens, such as the roughly contemporary *Prometheus*, the *Drunken Silenus* demonstrates a striking virtuosity in the overall manipulation of paint to achieve maximum effect from minimum effort, revealing a considerable degree of experience and technical skill. But the confident juxtaposition of Silenus' highly worked-up ear and cheeks with the barely altered grey ground of one side of his

moustache and beard is difficult to reconcile with the clumsy execution of the more poorly painted areas, such as the grapes at the upper right or the billowing parts of the young bacchante's sleeve,[14] a discrepancy clearly resulting from a collaboration between painters of different skills (Plate 5).

Other aspects of the execution also suggest a collaborative endeavour. The stem of the bunch of grapes held by Silenus is painted around the finished hand, and on close inspection can be seen to run slightly over its upper contour even as it is intended to be perceived as behind it, and therefore within his grasp (Plate 6). While conceivably a slight slip of the brush by the painter, it is more easily explained as the result of a still-life specialist adding a key iconographic element after the resolution of the figure; it is also interesting to note that the central grapes are of significantly higher quality than the crude, space-filling bunches at the upper right, which must have been the work of an inferior assistant. Also, while most of the dimpled rolls of fat in Silenus' flesh are carefully modelled, as can be seen around the elbow, similar features in the wrist are very summarily indicated with quite different unmodulated brown strokes in what it is tempting to explain as a correction or editing of the earlier execution by a different hand. More evidence of collaboration can be found in the fact that while most of the flesh painting of the principal figures is painted with a distinctive method of discernible parallel, hatched brushstrokes, only one part of the vegetation shows a similar technique – the fruit of the upper central pentimento mentioned earlier, which is also the only main vegetal element painted on top of the finished sky paint. This too makes sense as the late decision of the principal painter, perhaps unhappy with the effect of the negative space above Silenus or wishing to disguise an awkward transition between the night and dawn sky, himself altering the vegetation after the specialist still-life painter had finished the initial assignment.

While the picture itself suggests the participation of one principal artist working with the assistance or collaboration of at least two other painters, comparison with other works by Rubens and his associates is also necessary in the search for attribution. The chief inspiration for the National Gallery picture, albeit iconographic and not formal, is the version of the subject now in the Alte Pinakothek, Munich, of 1617/18–26, which is universally described as an autograph Rubens (Fig. 5). One writer has proposed that the Ovidian subject

Plate 6 (top left) *Drunken Silenus*. Detail of Silenus' left hand showing the stem of grapes painted over it.

Fig. 5 (top right) Peter Paul Rubens, *The Drunken Silenus*, 1617/18–26. Panel, 205 × 211 cm. Munich, Alte Pinakothek (no. 319).

Fig. 6 (above) Anthony van Dyck, *Samson and Delilah*, 1618–20. Canvas, 149 × 229.5 cm. Dulwich Picture Gallery (no. 127).

Fig. 7 (left) Anthony van Dyck, *Drunken Silenus with Faun and Bacchante*, 1618–20. Canvas, 133.5 × 109.5 cm. Brussels, Musées Royaux des Beaux-Arts de Belgique (no. 217).

Fig. 8 Anthony van Dyck, *Drunken Silenus*, 1620–1. Canvas, 107 × 91.5 cm. Dresden, Gemäldegalerie (no.1017).

Fig. 9 Anthony van Dyck, *Study Head of an Old Man with a White Beard*, 1617–20. Panel, 66 × 51.5 cm. New York, Metropolitan Museum of Art (no. 22.221).

matter had a deep and highly personal significance for Rubens,[15] although all that can be conclusively demonstrated is that he gave great attention to the panel, expanding the original half-length format in a series of stages to arrive at the final composition in a manner similar to that of his '*Watering Place*' (NG 4815) or *Sunset Landscape with a Shepherd and his Flock* (NG 2924) or the Prado *Three Graces*.[16] Like *Het Steen*, the Munich *Drunken Silenus* was in the artist's possession at his death.[17] Significantly for an understanding of the London picture, the Munich painting and its preparatory material were of major importance for the artist whom Rubens himself described as his best follower (*il meglior mio discepolo*), Anthony van Dyck.[18]

The exact date of Van Dyck's entry into the Rubens studio is uncertain,[19] but the two first met in 1613 when Van Dyck was fourteen years old. By 1618, having worked for some time in the studio, Van Dyck was established as an independent master, although he maintained close collaboration with Rubens until his departure for Italy in October 1621.[20] He was entrusted with an unusually high degree of responsibility, as is shown in a contract of 1620 in which he was given the main supervisory role for the execution of a series of thirty-nine paintings based on Rubens's designs for the ceiling of the Jesuit Church in Antwerp.[21]

Apart from his documented participation in various forms of collaborative effort within Rubens's studio, Van Dyck was also given the principal role in a number of commissions that were later extensively retouched by Rubens, such as the Prado *Achilles discovered among the Daughters of Lycomedes* (see p. 96 and Fig. 3).[22] He also habitually made his own more freely developed representations of subject paintings produced by Rubens, including *Moses and the Brazen Serpent*, *Susannah and the Elders*, *Saint Sebastian bound for Martyrdom*, *Samson and Delilah* (Fig. 6), the *Drunken Silenus* and a series of *Apostles*.

Van Dyck is generally agreed to be the painter of at least three versions of the Silenus subject: a now-destroyed *Drunken Silenus* formerly in the Kaiser Friedrich Museum, Berlin, the *Drunken Silenus with Faun and Bacchante* (Fig. 7) in the Musées Royaux des Beaux-Arts, Brussels, and the *Drunken Silenus* (Fig. 8) now in the Gemäldegalerie, Dresden. The Dresden version, recently dated to *c*.1620–1, is based on the first unexpanded version of Rubens's Munich picture; the Brussels picture is dated slightly earlier.[23]

It is reasonable also to include the National Gallery *Drunken Silenus* among the group of

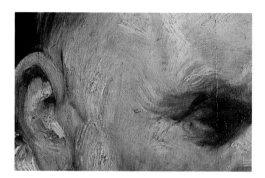

Plate 7 Van Dyck, *Study Head of an Old Man with a White Beard*. Detail showing distinctive parallel hatched modelling of flesh and hair.

Plate 8 *Drunken Silenus*. Detail from the old bacchante, showing a similar hatched modelling and handling of lakes in the eye socket; unlike the New York picture, much of the reddish-brown lake pigment has faded.

paintings largely or entirely made by Van Dyck. The fact that it is loosely based on the backward leaning figure in the Chantilly drawing is entirely consistent with the principal artist drawing inspiration from the range of sources at hand in the studio. Furthermore, the type, flesh tones, and general tonality of the young bacchante of the London *Silenus* (Plate 8) are strikingly similar to the Delilah figure in Van Dyck's Dulwich *Samson and Delilah*. Other critics have seen Van Dyck's style as being particularly evident in the head of the pipe player and satyr at right.[24] The distinctive hatched working of flesh paint throughout the picture is also clearly evident in Van Dyck's *Study Head of an Old Man with a White Beard* in New York (Fig. 9; Plate 7),[25] which also bears a remarkable similarity in the handling of the modelling of the eyes and eye sockets (here unfaded).

The argument for the principal authorship of Van Dyck rests on a combination of different kinds of evidence, much of which is circumstantial. The very nature of the Rubens studio, with its streamlined production and group participation, meant that painting techniques and materials were also largely uniform, which inevitably limits the ability of technical study to inform specific attributional questions. Knowledge of technique is of great importance, however, in understanding how these works were painted, if not always by whom, and gives some insight into the working dynamic among the members of the studio. In the absence of firm documentation, individual attributions continue to rely heavily on traditional style-based Morellian connoisseurship. When used together, however, both technical information and aesthetic judgements can aid the understanding of works like the *Drunken Silenus*; and the present study is therefore underpinned by a wider range of information than

was available earlier. If in the end we are still unsure of the finer points of authorship of parts of the painting, we can reflect that present uncertainty undoubtedly echoes that of some of Rubens's patrons and contemporaries.

Notes and references

1. Gregory Martin, *National Gallery Catalogues: The Flemish School 1600–1900*, London 1970, pp. 217–25.
2. Past analyses, consisting of microscopy and X-ray diffraction were undertaken by Véronique Tissières and Ashok Roy, while medium analyses by GC–MS and FTIR techniques were carried out by Raymond White.
3. See Arnout Balis, '"Fatto da un mio discepolo": Rubens' Studio Practices Reviewed', *Rubens and his Workshop: 'The Flight of Lot and his Family from Sodom'*, The National Museum of Western Art, Tokyo 1994, pp. 97–127, and *Corpus Rubenianum Ludwig Burchard, Part XVIII, II Hunting Scenes*, Oxford 1986, pp. 36–46, and Hans Vlieghe, 'Rubens' Atelier and History Painting in Flanders: A Review of the Evidence', *The Age of Rubens*, ed. Peter Sutton, Boston 1994, pp. 159–70.
4. See Josua Bruyn, 'The Rembrandt Workshop – function and production', *Rembrandt: The Master and his Workshop*, pp. 68–89, for examples of loosely conceived authorship within the Rembrandt shop.
5. In a letter of 11 May 1611, to Jacob de Bie: '...*ic over die hondert hebben moeten refuseren*' ('I have had to refuse over one hundred'). See Max Rooses and Ch. Ruelens, *Correspondence de Rubens*, Vol. II, 1898, pp. 35–6, and Ruth Saunders Magurn, *The Letters of Peter Paul Rubens*, Cambridge, Mass., 1955, p. 55.
6. Balis, cited in note 3, p. 110.
7. For the *Prometheus Bound* (Philadelphia Museum of Art, inv. no W50-3-1, oil on canvas, 243 × 210 cm): '*Un Prometheo legato sopra il monte Caucauso con una aquila che li becce il fegato. Originale da mia mano e*

l'aquila fatta da Snyders.' See also Peter Sutton, *Northern European Paintings in the Philadelphia Museum of Art*, Philadelphia 1990, pp. 251–61. The described leopard hunt is now lost: '*Leopardi cavati del naturale con satiri e nimfe. Originale de mia mano, eccetto un bellissimo paese fatto per mano di un valenthuomo in quel mestiere.*' The Prado *Achilles discovered among the Daughters of Lycomedes* (inv. no. 1661, oil on canvas, 246 × 267) is described as: '*Un quadro di un Achille vestito di donna fatto del meglior mio discepolo, i tutto ritocco de mia mano, quadro vaghissimo e pieno de molte fanciulle bellissime.*' See also Matías Díaz Padrón, *El Siglo de Rubens en el Museo del Prado: Catálago Razonado de Pintura [Flamenca del Siglo XVIII]*, Madrid 1995, pp. 1086–9. Rubens's letter quoted from Rooses and Ruelens, cited in note 5, II, pp. 135–44, and Magurn, cited in note 5, pp. 59–61, 441 (note 3).

8. Rooses and Ruelens, cited in note 5, II, p. 156. Also quoted in Susan J. Barnes, 'The Young Van Dyck and Rubens', *Anthony Van Dyck*, ed. A.K. Wheelock, S.J. Barnes and J.S. Held, exh. cat. National Gallery of Art, Washington DC 1990, p. 18.

9. Giovanni Pietro Bellori, *Le vite de' pittori, scultori et architetti moderne*, Rome 1672, p. 254; Joachim von Sandrart, *Der Teutschen Academie der edlen Bau-Bild- und Mahleren Künste*, Nürnberg 1675, p. 157; Roger de Piles, *Abregé de la vie des peintres, avec des réflexions sur leurs ouvrages (seconde edition)*, Paris 1699, pp. 396–7.

10. This development can be seen in the history of scholarship of the *Drunken Silenus* itself in the way that technical information gleaned from the 1946 restoration, incorporated in the 1947 National Gallery catalogue of *An Exhibition of Cleaned Pictures (1936–1947)*, was used in the 1970 National Gallery school catalogue. See Martin, cited in note 1, pp. 217–18 and 221.

11. The use of an oil medium, rather than glue, for chalk has not been extensively documented but may be more common than had been supposed. It has been found on the National Gallery's *Portrait of a Woman and Child* (NG 3011, 131.5 × 106 cm) by Anthony van Dyck.

12. Any carbonaceous material used in preparatory drawing would be effectively swamped by the extensive carbon black in the grey layer of the preparation, while the density of the lead white from that same layer, as well as the subsequent working of many light and dense areas of the painting, would probably overwhelm the traces of any painted drawing in the X-radiograph.

13. Identified by Jo Kirby using microspectrophotometry as an insect dyestuff, probably cochineal.

14. The sleeve drapery may have been crudely reworked in a very early restoration. Although it has developed a similar craquelure to the rest of the painting, it is the only area sampled on the picture to have used non-heat-bodied linseed oil as the principal constituent of the paint medium (except for white flesh highlights, which were painted in the less yellowing walnut oil, which was however also heat-bodied). All other samples taken were found to have been painted in heat-bodied linseed oil, with the addition of a trace of pine resin in brown samples taken from shadowed areas of the old bacchante's head.

15. See Svetlana Alpers, 'Creativity in the Flesh: The "Drunken Silenus"', *The Making of Rubens*, New Haven 1995, pp. 101–57.

16. See Christopher Brown, *Making and Meaning: Rubens's Landscapes*, exh. cat., London 1996, pp. 52–5, 95–103 and 116–21, and George Bisacca and José de la Fuente, 'Consideracciones técnicas de la construcción y restauración del soporte de las Tres Gracias de Rubens', *Las 'Tres Gracias' de Rubens: Estudio técnico y Restauración*, Madrid 1998, pp. 51–8.

17. See *Alte Pinakothek München: Erläuterungen zu den austellten Gemälden*, Munich 1983, pp. 453–4.

18. Rooses and Ruelens, cited in note 5, II, p. 137, and Magurn, cited in note 5, pp. 61, 441.

19. See Margaret Roland, 'Van Dyck's Early Workshop, The "Apostle" Series, and the "Drunken Silenus"', *Art Bulletin*, LXVI, no. 2, 1984, pp. 211–23.

20. See Roland, cited in note 19, p. 216, and Barnes, cited in note 8, p. 18.

21. '*Ten tweeden dat den voors. Sr Rubens de teekeninge van alle de voors. 39 stucken sal gehouden syn met eygen handt in't cleyne te maken, ende door Van Dyck mitsgaders sommige adere syne disipelen soo in't groot te doen opwerken*' (the above named Senor Rubens shall make all the above named thirty-nine pieces in small format in his own hand, from which Van Dyck and other of his pupils shall work them up in the full scale), in J. Rupert Martin, *Corpus Rubenianum Ludwig Burchard I: The Ceiling Paintings for the Jesuit Church in Antwerp*, p. 214.

22. Rubens does not actually use Van Dyck's name, but his description of the collaborative artist as 'the best of my pupils' (*il meglior mio discepolo*) is universally understood to describe the young Van Dyck. See Rooses and Ruelens, cited in note 5, II, p. 137, Magurn, cited in note 5, pp. 61, 441, Vlieghe, cited in note 3, p. 161, and Balis, cited in note 3, p. 110.

23. See Barnes, 'Drunken Silenus' (catalogue entry of the picture now in the Gemäldegalerie, Dresden), in *Anthony Van Dyck*, cited in note 8, p. 106.

24. Martin, cited in note 1, pp. 217–19, and personal communication from Christopher Brown.

25. See Walter Liedtke, *Flemish Paintings in the Metropolitan Museum of Art*, 1984, pp. 64–7. The picture is given a date of 1617–20, which accords well with the National Gallery picture. I am grateful to George Bisacca, Associate Paintings Conservator at the Metropolitan Museum, for making photographic details of the painting.